Warning!

Violence, War, Magic & the Supernatural

The fictional world of Rifts® is violent, deadly and filled with supernatural monsters. Other-dimensional beings often referred to as "demons," torment, stalk and prey on humans. Other alien life forms, monsters, gods and demigods, as well as magic, insanity, and war are all elements in this book.

Some parents may find the violence, magic and supernatural elements of the game inappropriate for young readers/players. We suggest parental discretion.

Please note that none of us at Palladium Books® condone or encourage the occult, the practice of magic, the use of drugs, or violence.

A Rifts® Adventure Sourcebook.
An overview of the Chi-Town 'Burbs & the 'Burb of Firetown

Dedication

To Alex Marciniszyn and *Wayne Smith*. One longtime editor and one more recent. Both of these gents help to keep me on track and make my words look good. More importantly, both are cherished friends who are always there when I need them. Thanks for everything from then to now, and for years to come.

– Kevin Siembieda, 2003

Also for Rifts® ...

Rifts® Adventure Sourcebook: Firetown & the Tolkeen Crisis

Rifts® Adventure Sourcebook: The Black Vault™

Rifts® Adventure Sourcebook: The Vanguard™

Revised Rifts® Conversion Book One

Rifts® Dark Conversions (Nightbane, demons & more).

Rifts® Bionics Sourcebook

Rifts® Phase World®: Guide to the Three Galaxies™

Rifts® Phase World®: Anvil Galaxy™

Rifts® Game Master Guide™

Rifts® Book of Magic™

Rifts® Aftermath™

Rifts® Adventure Guide™

Rifts® Coalition Wars (Tolkeen) #1-6

The Rifter® Sourcebook series and more.

The cover is by *Mark Evans*. It depicts a Ley Line Walker or Earth Warlock using magic to strike Coalition soldiers with rocks in the hope of making good an escape.

First Printing – March 2003

Palladium Books® Presents:

Chi-Town 'Burbs
Adventure Sourcebook

Written by: **Kevin Siembieda**

Some additional text & ideas by: **Julius Rosenstein**
Alex Marciniszyn

Editors: **Alex Marciniszyn**
Wayne Smith

Proofreader: **Julius Rosenstein**

Cover Painting: **Mark Evans**

Interior Artists: **Wayne Breaux Jr.**
Kent Burles
Apollo Okamura
Freddie Williams
Michael Wilson

Art Direction & Keylining: **Kevin Siembieda**

Typography: **Wayne Smith**

Special Thanks to Alex, Julius, and Wayne for their input on this project; Apollo "Transformers" Okamura and Freddie "I'm there" Williams for their artistic endeavors. And, as always, to Palladium's hard working and heroic staff.

– *Kevin Siembieda, 2003*

Contents

Quick Find

Life in the Burbs: Forbidden Knowledge & Secrets

The first step to new adventures

Welcome to the first **Rifts® Adventure Sourcebook** – a series where we plan to delve into parts of the world we have yet to explore, many of which actually exist in familiar territory. People like Emperor and Joseph Prosek, artificial people like Archie-3, organizations like the Vanguard and the Republicans, places like the new fortress city of New Waukegan, and shadowy corners of the world like the nooks and crannies of the Chi-Town 'Burbs and the Black Vault are all about to be laid out for your enjoyment. All are familiar names and places that remain nebulous and unknown even though they have helped to shape the region or play an important role on Rifts Earth. Each of these Adventure Sourcebooks should open up entire new realms of adventure on a smaller and more intimate scale.

Our starting point is the *Coalition State of Chi-Town* and the many people, places and stories born from its existence. Why Chi-Town? Because it is the heart and schizophrenic soul of human civilization in North America. Because whether one likes it or not, the continent would be a very different place without the Coalition States or without Chi-Town at its epicenter. Chi-Town's history, leaders and actions have helped to shape the region, giving rise to the Coalition States, Free Quebec and many kingdoms that were inspired by it or became its antithesis, like the Federation of Magic, Lazlo, the Pecos Empire, and the late Tolkeen, among others. Chi-Town's very existence, politics, actions and leaders – particularly its Emperor – inspire and motivate millions, even if half the time that motivation is born from fear or hate. In fact, many kingdoms and individuals have risen up to challenge, oppose or offer an alternative lifestyle to the Coalition's oppressive ideals, but the CS is still their motivating factor, the reason they came into being or took a particular stance. Furthermore, whatever path the CS takes creates ripples (sometimes shock waves) that affect every kingdom and nation within 3000 miles (4800 km). The war and fall of Tolkeen is just one recent and dramatic example of the Coalition States' legacy of influence, power and terror.

The first several **Rifts® Adventure Sourcebooks** take an in-depth look at the people who live directly in Chi-Town's shadow, the inhabitants of the *Chi-Town 'Burbs*. Portions of the 'Burbs will be mapped, many of its notable inhabitants, movers and shakers examined, and some of its dark corners exposed for the very first time. In the process, stories of individuals and groups will unfold to bring the lives of these people into sharper focus and present numerous opportunities for exploration, adventure and heroics.

Adventure is a prominent part of the title, because each book should include one or more adventures built around the subject of that title, as well as present information, people and settings from which many additional adventures can be spun on your own. Some **Rifts® Adventure Sourcebooks** will be heavily adventure driven while others, like this first one, may paint a broader picture, laying the groundwork for adventures and present a setting rather than an outright adventure. However, even setting- and people-based books shall offer platforms for building your own adventures.

Future Rifts® Adventure Sourcebooks will include *more on the 'Burbs* and its many stories as well as *Tolkeen Retribution Squads, the Vanguard, the Black Vault, the Ruins of Old Chicago, the Great Library, the Prosek Family* and *more*. Other Adventure Sourcebooks will take place away from Chi-Town, including the *Fortress City of New Waukegan, the Republicans, Archie Three, Demon-held Detroit, Tolkeen (in the aftermath of war), Splugorth Slavers, Federation of Magic,* and *overseas*. Each book is designed to be a quick read and an easy to use 48-64 pages (maybe the occasional 96 pager) focusing on one particular subject. And while many may be set in, or start from, the same location, each will go in a different direction, tackle a new idea or subject matter, and stand complete in itself (no cliffhanger continued stories). We hope to produce these little gems on a monthly or bi-monthly basis, which means Palladium is likely to let some (or all) eventually go out of print as new titles take their place.

So join us on new travels and adventures. Bring your friends along too, you may need all the help you can get.

– Kevin Siembieda, March 2003

Chi-Town 'Burbs – Today
Summer 109 P.A.

The *Kingdom of Tolkeen* has only recently fallen (days or a couple of weeks). Word of its collapse has already sent Chi-Town and the 'Burbs buzzing like an excited beehive.

Security in and around the great fortress city of *Chi-Town* has been increased ten-fold (and it was super-tight to begin with). Visiting passes have been severely restricted (reduced by 90%; indefinitely), sky patrols tripled, police and military presence doubled and a general uneasiness hangs in the air. Worry about possible repercussions on Coalition soil for Tolkeen's destruction is omnipresent. To ensure the safety of Emperor Prosek, he and his family have limited their public appearances and *each* has been assigned an additional security squad to escort them everywhere. **A typical security squad** is made up of elite troops as follows: A trusted human Psychic (usually a Psi-Net "Spotter"), two Dog Boy "Psi-Hounds" from NTSET and two human or Psi-Stalker NTSET Protectors as defense against magic and the supernatural, plus two SAMAS, two CS Cyborg Strike Troopers or Coalition Juicers, and two experienced Soldiers/Grunts, in addition to electronic security measures and undercover agents nearby.

Emotions in the 'Burbs are much more raw and openly displayed. They boil with stories about Tolkeen's fall, the final siege, notable people, and what comes next. The emotions are mixed. Angry and frightened voices are heard from open windows, while cheers of joy, shouts of victory, cries of protest and tears of relief all fill the streets. The immediate reaction among the people of the 'Burbs is just that intense and diverse. But there is something else: an air of lingering anticipation as if something big is about to happen.

Josephton, the oldest of the boot-licking Old Town 'Burbs, declares a national holiday and celebrates the great victory to "make us all safe from magic and Hell spawn" as if it were New Year's Eve for a week. **Prosekville**, the richest of the Old Town 'Burbs, behaves similarly, though with more reserve and class. In fact, most of the Old Town 'Burbs, filled with loyalists and prime candidates for citizenship to the *City of Chi-Town* or *New Waukegan,* cheer, parade, celebrate and send congratulatory messages to Emperor Prosek and the people of the Coalition States. **New Colfax** is the quietest of the Old Towns, **Little Chi-Town** the noisiest, and even the machine shops, factories and furnaces of **Ironforge** are shut down for two days in honor of the victory and to allow people to celebrate and reflect.

Things are much wilder in the New Towns and Shanty Towns.

Rioting and attacks on Coalition Forces erupt in the New Town 'Burb of **Tranquility** and two neighboring shanty towns. The riots rage for three days until the Coalition Army sweeps down and obliterates the two shanty towns in less than 90 minutes. Truth be told, though word of Tolkeen's fall sparked the initial rioting, things quickly spilled out of hand as people began looting and rioting just for the thrill of it, with certain individuals trying to profit from it, or extract anonymous revenge on old rivals and enemies under the cover of the riots.

Elsewhere in the 'Burbs, humanoid predators and opportunists begin to stir, sensing opportunity and money on the wind. The unofficial 'Burb police, protectors and vigilantes prepare for trouble as adventurers, lowlifes and others flutter out of their roosts and take wing to capitalize on the loss, despair and hatred of others, waiting, circling, like hungry vultures. Everyone, good and evil, self-serving or selfless, gets ready for the aftermath of war – for the shock wave of humanity, treasure, secrets and horror that is inevitably on its way.

There hasn't been this much activity and excitement in years, and it is making the Chi-Town authorities nervous. Very nervous.

A Brief Overview of the Chi-Town 'Burbs

Old Towns

Ironforge: The third oldest of the Old Town 'Burbs (68 years old) is filled with heavy industry factories and foundries. Racial mix is 92% human, 2% Psi-Stalker and 6% D-Bee; 10% are literate. They are hardworking loyalists and dreamers who are certain some of their citizens will be picked for citizenship in Chi-Town or New Waukegan thanks to their work ethics and conviction.

Josephton: The oldest Old Town 'Burb (it is 80 years old and built on a site where a shanty town existed for 16 years prior). Super-loyal to Chi-Town, the Prosek family & the Coalition States. These inhabitants are staunch human supremacists who refuse to use D-Bees even as slave labor. Known to cooperate openly and fully with the Coalition authorities at Chi-Town. Racial mix is 100% human (even Psi-Stalkers are looked down upon); 25% are literate.

Little Chi-Town: The newest and most irreverent of the Old Town 'Burbs (only about 38 years old). Has a 15 foot (4.6 m) stone wall (half is made of M.D.C. materials) around it, with gate towers and independent police force/defenders. It is a mix of light industrial and residential. Racial mix is 96% human and 4% D-Bee; 40% are literate.

New Colfax: An Old Town built around a foundation of factories and industry. Most residents are working class, loyal to the CS and Chi-Town, but they also voice their frustration about the slow turning wheels of CS bureaucracy and the injustices of the no-man's zone that is the 'Burbs. Many also question the Coalition's stance against magic of any kind, and rumor suggests the Vanguard may have its foundation in this 'Burb. (That is, if one believes in the urban myth about a secret enclave of sorcerers loyal to the CS who quietly work for its benefit.) Racial mix is 93.5% human, 2.5% Psi-Stalker and 4% D-Bee; 8% are literate. 53 years old.

Prosekville: The second oldest (76 years old) and richest Old Town 'Burb. Super-loyal to Chi-Town, the Prosek Family and the Coalition States. Half are dedicated human supremacists, the other half are quietly more tolerant (toward D-Bees and magic) as long as they profit from their efforts. Racial mix is 96% human, 2% Psi-Stalker, and 2% D-Bee; 15% are literate.

New Towns

Center Court: Is quickly becoming an intermediary for trade and business between the Shanty Towns and other New Towns with the Old Towns and outsiders looking to trade. Racial mix is 80% human and 20% D-Bee; 30% are literate.

Firetown: A typical mix of light industry, residential and free enterprise. It is notorious for its fires. Half or more of the town has burnt down on three occasions and there have been six significant fires over the last 13 years (and numerous minor incidents). Ironically, this has prompted Firetown to form the best fire and rescue department in the Chi-Town 'Burbs, using conventional technology as well as magical means (i.e., Techno-Wizard water guns and rain flares, magic spells and the aid of Water and Fire Warlocks). Racial mix is 85% human and 15% D-Bee; 15% are literate. **Note:** Firetown is the 'Burb we are going to map and describe in detail for this book and subsequent Adventure Sourcebooks as an example of a "typical" New Town 'Burb.

Harmony: A mix of light industry, residential and free enterprise. Racial mix is 85% human and 15% D-Bee; 10-15% are literate.

Hope: A typical mix of light industry, residential and free enterprise. Racial mix is 82% human and 18% D-Bee; less than 10% are literate. As the name suggests, many of its residents hold on to a deep, abiding hope and trust that they will find a better life as citizens of Chi-Town or New Waukegan.

Staunton Heights: The richest of the New Town 'Burbs, this is where the most successful (and conniving) adventurers, retired mercenaries, smugglers, merchants, business owners, and white collar workers live when they can't get into one of the Old Towns or the fortress city. It actually has manicured parks, fountains, an M.D.C. town hall and courthouse, and a number of large, nice homes, many with lawns and picket fences. Its police force is diligent about keeping law and order and is known to cooperate openly and fully with the Coalition authorities at Chi-Town. Consequently, crime is the lowest of any New Town and the Black Market has a minimal presence. Racial mix is 90% human and 10% D-Bee; 32% are literate.

Stockyard: This town is mostly working class residential and industrial. Smoke belching factories, junkyards, lumberyards, used vehicle lots and warehouses are its most distinguishing features. Residences are small houses and shabby apartment buildings, the inhabitants rough and tumble, but mostly hardworking and god fearing. Seventy-five percent are human and 25% D-Bees, most of the latter are the big, strong types who engage in heavy labor and are treated as a secret sub-class of slave-like workers. Only about 6% are literate. The CS turns a blind eye to these inhuman laborers provided they hold no positions of power and know their place, i.e. are subservient to humans and bow down to CS authorities. Those who stand out or defy the CS are beaten into submission or cut down.

Tranquility: Is the wildest of the New Towns. It has suffered several Coalition purges, the most recent only a few days ago to quell riots the local authorities could not handle. Chi-Town authorities have had their fill of this lawless 'Burb and are considering putting an end to it once and for all. In the meanwhile, the CS is keeping a close eye on this seedy town. There is an increased Police/ISS presence with independent Coalition Army patrols (both in the air and on the ground), and rumor has it a large number of CS operatives have gone undercover. Word on the street is that the only reason the CS hasn't flattened Tranquility is because it has its own network of spies entrenched in the community providing valuable intelligence on the place and criminal (and terrorist) activities throughout the 'Burbs.

The only place more decadent than Tranquility is Mayhem, but that Shanty Town is under such tight control by the Black Market and criminals under the Market's thumb, that it is comparatively tame, at least on its public face. Tranquility, on the other hand, seems to erupt in violence on a daily a basis. Gunfights, shootings, stabbings, duels, brawls, gang clashes, arson, displays of magic, monsters on the rampage, and all manner of trouble are daily occurrences in the town that is anything but tranquil. Prostitution, drug deals and other illegal activities are conducted out in the open, Cyber-Snatcher gangs prowl the streets along with other street gangs and predators. The walls of its alleys and many business establishments are covered in graffiti – much of it anti-Coalition States – and panhandlers, drunks and bums are a frequent obstacle in the streets, especially late in the night and wee hours of the morning. Racial mix is 70% human and 30% D-Bee; less than 5% are literate.

Shanty Towns

The Frontier: The newest outlying shanty town; *two months old*. Mostly residential, well, people living out of the back of their vehicles, in tents and shabby huts. Racial mix is 75% human and 25% D-Bee; less than 5% are literate.

Gravel Town: Also known as "Pit Town" and "The Pits" because it is built in and around an old gravel pit. Mostly residential. Tunnels and underground dwellings plus Pueblo Indian style dwellings line the walls of the town/gravel pit. *Four years old* and this is actually its third incarnation, with half the place being destroyed on two different occasions, one an "accident," the other a Coalition purge. Racial mix is 70% human and 30% D-Bee; 25% are literate.

Hodgepodge: Also known as "The Hodge" and "Podge Town" interchangeably. It had a different name when it was founded, but no one can remember what it might have been, and folks prefer the ones it is known by today, anyway. There are no streets that run in a straight line in the Hodge or that don't stop in a dead end. It is very easy to get lost here. Podge Town is home to a good number of illegal operations, and the Black Market, Juicers, Mercenaries and City Rats have a strong presence and influence. *Two years old.* Racial mix is 80% human and 20% D-Bee; 12% are literate.

Mayhem: The town that never sleeps. Locals like to think visiting Mayhem is rather like stepping into the Wild West, complete with noisy saloons and shoot outs in the street. Most places of entertainment are open around the clock and most other businesses from 9:00 A.M. till 10:00 or 12:00 P.M. The town is home to a lot of bars/taverns, dance halls, nightclubs, gambling casinos, blind pigs (small, private saloons and gambling places for underworld figures and those with connections), theaters (live, film and competitions like boxing and wrestling), underground movie theaters (show illegal, ancient pre-Rifts movies and TV shows), prostitution, drug dens, Psi-Cola flop houses, pit arenas (illegal gladiatorial arenas and animal fights), and so on. Almost *three years old*. Racial mix is 65% human and 35% D-Bee; roughly 15% are literate. The CS keeps its eye on this 'Burb.

Outer Watch: Popular among warrior and adventurer types, including Psi-Stalkers. *10 months old*. Racial mix is 50% human, 35% Psi-Stalker (mutant humans) and 15% D-Bee; less than 5% are literate.

Roadside: Built along the side of one of the M.D.C. roads that leads to Chi-Town. *18 months old*. Racial mix is 85% human and 15% D-Bee; less than 8% are literate.

Eastwood: *Six months old*. Built on the bones of Harveston which existed on this spot before it was destroyed by fire, just like the six shanty towns that came before it. Racial mix is 72% human and 28% D-Bee; less than 5% are literate.

Razor Ridge: *Nine months old*, it was Kelly's Ridge, a year old Shanty Town until it was taken over by the *Razor Crimm Gang*, a company of mercenaries known to work for the Coalition Army as scouts and Special Forces "freelancers." In fact, *Wolverine Crimm* (one of Razor's sons) and some of his boys pulled reconnaissance and Black Ops for the CS in Tolkeen until about six months ago. They had their fill and left shortly before the infamous Sorcerers' Revenge, but rumor has it they participated in the "scorched earth" part of General Drogue's *Operation Hardball*, though none of them talk much about their "tour of duty in Tolkeen." Racial mix of the town is 84% human and 16% D-Bee; about 15% are literate.

Snake's Skin and **Camp Generation Next**, near the New Town of *Tranquility*, have been recently purged and expunged from existence by Coalition forces with no tolerance for insurrection. Though an extreme measure, their obliteration put an instant stop to the rioting in and around Tranquility, and quelled any similar notions in the other 'Burbs. Residents who happened to escape the razing of these two Shanty Towns, along with scavengers and thieves, sift through the charred rubble looking for what few valuables and personal items may have survived. It is likely to be at least six months before two new Shanty Towns are erected on these locations, though a few dozen tents have already been pitched. Racial mix for each was 65% human and 35% D-Bee. Estimated casualties from the purge: 25% of all humans and 70% of all D-Bee inhabitants.

Living in a state of limbo
'Burbs, the communities that don't exist

The Coalition Government, never one to miss an opportunity, has made the 'Burbs a weird *nonentity*. Unlike other cities, towns and communities found throughout the Coalition States, the 'Burbs are NOT recognized as a legal entity. Instead they are each considered an illegal community of squatters without any claim to the land they inhabit or any of the normal rights enjoyed by the average CS citizens all around them. Desperate and/or blinded by the dream of paradise that life as a big city dweller promises, most people in the 'Burbs (90%) accept this legal limbo as a consequence of the path they have chosen. After all, most of these people have risked everything, including their lives, just to get here in the first place.

What this means is those who choose to live in the 'Burbs have no rights. None. Those born in the rural and wilderness areas of the Coalition States are born with the rights of CS citizenship, but they also give up those rights if they move to the 'Burbs, becoming a nebulous *nonentity* for the promise of a better life in the fortress city. Normally, any *humans* born within lands claimed by the CS are presumed to be citizens and expected to accept the Emperor as their leader and the Coalition Government as the law of the land. Those who do not are considered traitorous rabble, barbarians, or rebellious malcontents and dealt with accordingly. The people living in the 'Burbs are neither citizens or malcontents, for they desire to live in the CS but in a fortified city. To get that special, elite living environment, they accept the nonexistent limbo that is the 'Burbs, where they have no value or rights in the eyes of the Coalition Government until they are accepted as a citizen of the fortress city or leave the 'Burbs to find citizenship in one of the other (non-walled) CS cities, towns or rural communities.

The fact that the 'Burbs are unrecognized as a legal township, city or community of any kind gives the CS government and military absolute power over those living there. Consequently, the Coalition military and local city authorities (from the fortress city) can do pretty much anything they want to the "squatters" and "rejects" in the 'Burbs. Furthermore, it is the fortress city that owns the land on which the 'Burbs are located.

All this means the local and national CS governments can harass, interrogate, arrest, beat, and even murder people and bulldoze entire city blocks if they so choose, because the people of the 'Burbs have forsaken their rights as recognized citizens. Crazy? Yeah, like a fox. The Coalition government uses the unique situation of the 'Burbs to their advantage in countless ways.

For one, it enables them to attract, keep tabs on and infiltrate scores of criminal, mercenary and opposition groups using the 'Burbs as their base of operations, as well as those groups who come to visit or trade at the 'Burbs (adventurer groups included).

For another, the Coalition's secret agents and visible CS police and army troops operating in the 'Burbs are able to identify

practitioners of magic, unregistered psychics, smugglers, rebels, criminals, adventurers and other "undesirables." To help them in their task of identifying and gathering intelligence on these undesirables, they utilize a network of gung-ho informants living in the 'Burbs, all hoping to win the authorities' favor to get themselves or family members "fast-tracked" into the fortress city.

Third, the Coalition Military attracts thousands of new recruits with the *implied promise* that anyone who serves in the military will *earn* themselves and their immediate family special consideration for citizenship in the city, as well as get them moved to the top of the waiting list. Of course, no such promise is ever put in writing. It is implied and understood with a wink and a nod. This practice gets them thousands of volunteers joining the Coalition Army annually. These Burbie dupes played a big role in the siege against Tolkeen and the war on Free Quebec as they served as front-line troops in both campaigns.

Fourth, the 'Burbs provide the CS with a cheap labor force living in such deplorable third-world conditions that they are willing to take almost any job at cut rates to feed themselves or support their families.

Fifth, the 'Burbs provide a constant source of *volunteers* for all kinds of dangerous tasks, from agreeing to test new medicines, vaccines and experimental treatments to wilderness reconnaissance and spy missions.

It is also rumored that the Coalition States, particularly the City of Chi-Town, conducts secret experiments on sectors of the 'Burb population. Everything from testing the response to new propaganda to testing psychological warfare/manipulation, experimental military weapons, and even testing biological agents (plagues).

Remember, the inhabitants of the 'Burbs are *not* citizens of the allied States. They are unauthorized and unrecognized communities that have *invaded* the Coalition States. Their problems are not the concern of the Coalition States. Its people have no rights, no claim to land, and exist in a political no-man's zone. The majority of inhabitants are undesirables, rejects or squatters who are *non-entities* in the eyes of the Coalition. The CS does not acknowledge any government, ruling body, organization or leader that may rise from the 'Burbs. Any declaration of independence or sovereignty is an act of war! Consequently, the Coalition Military and government can tear a 'Burb down and/or harass its inhabitants whenever they want to. Remember, the inhabitants of the 'Burbs are not CS citizens and their communities are not recognized as any sort of political entity, so they have absolutely no rights! Thus, the CS Army can enter a 'Burb, burst into a home or business, trash the place, threaten any of its people, and beat, rape and even kill inhabitants with impunity. Any resistance on the part of the "Burbies" or attacks leveled against the CS authorities can only instigate serious trouble. Riots, destruction of a neighborhood or wholesale slaughter are the least of the probable aftermath of a confrontation with the CS Military or ISS.

Slang Terms Common to the 'Burbs

Black Mark: As in, "has a black mark," meaning someone is marked by the Black Market for capture and questioning, or marked for death ("Death Mark" or "Black Death Mark")!

Those "marked" may have a bounty on their heads, but turning over those marked who do not have a reward (which is about half) may earn the person or group the recognition and/or favor of the Black Market, or at least that particular faction or group leader.

Black Shop: A business owned or run by the Black Market and which probably offers contraband and illegal services or knows who does. Black Shops run the gamut from gambling establishments, saloons, drug dens, houses of prostitution, fencers, smuggling rings, forgery operations, and worse, to dealers in weapons, armor, magic, books and contraband, and legitimate businesses.

Body-Chop-Shop: A Black Market cybernetics facility that sells, installs, and implants bionics and cybernetics. Most can perform partial bionic reconstruction, repairs and implants. Only the best can perform full bionic conversion or install major artificial organs like the heart and lungs. Most Body-Chop-Shops also buy stolen and *used* bionics, giving rise to roving gangs of cutthroats known as *Cyber-Snatchers* who attack people to steal their bionics, usually maiming or killing and butchering their victims in the process. Both the Body-Chop-Shops and Cyber-Snatchers are found in the 'Burbs.

'Burb: A town or city of *squatters* outside a large Coalition city, typically a fortress city like Chi-Town, who hope to petition the State for residence in the fortress city.

Burbie: Somebody who takes up residence in a 'Burb. Also see "Reject."

City Rat: A general term for youths and gangs of youths who are technophiles (love technology and cybernetics) and who know the city better than most. Many are computer hackers, information dealers, runners and small-time crooks. See the **Rifts® Bionics Sourcebook** for the *City Rat "redefined"* and complete stats for the *City Rat Archetype, Hero Rat, Hack Rat, Maze Rat, Pack Rat, Gutter Rat* (killers and Cyber-Snatchers), and the *Roof Rat*, as well as *Cyber-Snatchers* (villains).

Cyber-Doc: A medical doctor and surgeon who specializes in installing, repairing, upgrading and implanting cybernetics and bionics. Common at Body-Chop-Shops.

Cyber-Snatchers: Roving gangs of murderers who target people with bionics and rob them of their cybernetics, usually killing their victims in the process. See **Rifts® Bionics Sourcebook**, page 26, for complete stats and greater info.

D-Bee: Short for "Dimensional Being," typically referring to any humanoid or bipedal alien from another world.

Dark-House: Slang for underground movie theaters that show illegal, pre-Rifts films and television shows banned by the CS. They are also known as "historyplexes" and "sin-o-plexes."

Dead Boy: Typically refers to soldiers in the Coalition Military, so named for their black, skeleton motif body armor, and their habit of shooting suspects and troublemakers "dead."

Dead Head: A Coalition soldier or police officer willing to take bribes (money, favors, goods, etc.) to look the other way – i.e. a "dead head" who sees nothing. The more serious the offense the more costly the bribe.

Dog Boy: The Coalition's famous canine troops – part dog, part human.

Downsider: A term to describe residents of the big city who live on one of the lower levels.

Fed or Federal: Slang for someone from, working with or connected to the Federation of Magic. ("I'd watch out for him, I hear he's a Federal.")

From Beyond the Rift: Typically refers to someone who came through a dimensional portal/Rift from another world or dimension. May be a "D-Bee" or a supernatural being or creature of magic.

G-Club: The nickname for the Park Gentleman's Club in Firetown. A reputed hangout for organized crime bosses and big shots from throughout the Chi-Town 'Burbs.

Grunger: A resident of the big city, but one who is a low life involved in a gang or with crime, City Rats or the 'Burbs or Burbies.

I.C.: Identification Coding for psychics. All psychics living in the Coalition States, including those in the 'Burbs, are supposed to participate in the Psychic Registration Program (PRP) in which they get an Identification Code (bar code) and I.D. implant.

Inkslinger: A tattoo artist.

I.S.S. a.k.a. "The Eyes": I.S.S. stands for Internal Security Specialists, an elite Coalition States law enforcement and internal security organization that is the equivalent combination of the F.B.I., C.I.A. and Homeland security agents. It is their job to keep Coalition cities safe, and that means keeping an eye on the 'Burbs and nipping terrorists, saboteurs, practitioners of magic, and superhumans from threatening CS citizens. See **Rifts® World Book 11: Coalition War Campaign** for complete details.

I.S.S. 'Specter: An Internal Security Specialist *Inspector*, basically the equivalent combination of the F.B.I., C.I.A. and Homeland Security agent rolled into one.

Lawman: A police officer or sheriff that is NOT affiliated with the Coalition States, i.e. a sheriff from a kingdom outside the CS.

LL or Low Leveler: Another term for residents of the fortified city, who live on the lowest levels. An elite status that many Burbies would love to achieve (at least from their point of view).

Mage: A generic term for any practitioner of magic, but usually refers to some sort of *spell caster*. Thus, a Necromancer or Shifter would be referred to as such, while a Ley Line Walker, Warlock, Mystic, or other spell caster (often including Techno-Wizards) is a "mage."

New Town: The newer, middle laying 'Burbs that grow up around the Old Towns.

NTSET a.k.a. "Nut Set": An elite division of "psychic police" and "monster hunters" within the I.S.S. Sometimes referred to as "psychic police." See **Rifts® World Book 11: Coalition War Campaign** for details.

Old Town: The oldest and most city-like of the 'Burbs.

Old Townee: An inhabitant of an Old Town 'Burb.

Paper Inker: Slang for a forger or underground operation that manufactures fake identification cards, travel papers, etc.; typically a Black Market operation.

Psi-Hound: A NTSET Dog Boy trained specifically to sniff out, recognize and counter psychic, supernatural and magical threats.

Reject: Someone who has applied for citizenship in a fortified city and has been rejected. The rejection of a city application is usually permanent and irrevocable, but many Rejects stay to live in the 'Burbs, and many still cling to their dream of life in the big city if only they could find some way to prove themselves worthy. "Reject" is sometimes used by I.S.S. and Coalition Military troops as a derogatory term for ALL inhabitants of the 'Burbs,.

Retribution Squads: Typically sorcerers, freedom fighters, terrorists and vengeful citizens or monsters from the fallen Kingdom of Tolkeen seeking revenge against the Coalition States, in general, and the Coalition Army, Chi-Town and the Prosek family in particular. They may engage in sabotage, vandalism, attacks on CS authority figures, murder, bombings, suicide bombings, sniping, assassination, kidnaping, extortion and other acts of revenge and damage against the CS.

Shanty Town: The newest shabby communities springing up around the New Towns. They are part tent city, part refugee camp and part trailer park.

Sin-o-plex: Slang for underground movie theaters that show illegal, pre-Rifts films and television shows banned by the CS. They are also known as "historyplexes" and "dark-houses."

Stoolie or Stool Pigeon: An individual who makes a living or regularly earns favors from the CS or other organization by providing them with information about people, places and goings on in the 'Burbs. A City Rat who is a Stool Pigeon is known as a "Roof Rat" or "Rat Fink."

Tarnits: People who are fans and promoters of the famed historian, Erin Tarn.

Tolkeenite: The name of people who once resided as citizens in the Kingdom of Tolkeen.

A Brief Overview of 'Burb Society

The fortified cities of the Coalition States, of which Chi-Town was the first and, arguably, the greatest, represent a safe haven for humans. A refuge and urban paradise for humans who live within its Mega-Damage walls without fear of attack from invaders, monsters, demons, aliens or marauding sorcerers or raiders. Each citizen is given a job and finds his or her place in CS society. The people live a life of comparative high-tech luxury and civility. All apartments and businesses have hot and cold running water, reliable electrical power, heating and cooling systems, secure telephone network, city-wide internet access, modern conveniences of every kind, social interaction, and even leisure time and entertainment by way of CS television, film theaters, concert halls, live theater, museums, diners, sporting events and all the things one imagines an advanced megalopolis would have to offer.

Most importantly, the government and economy are stable and the leadership works to provide for and protect its citizens like few others on Rifts Earth. Law and order are enforced to provide a safe and secure place to live, work and raise a family. As basic as all this may sound, such amenities, security and lei-sure are truly rare commodities in North America and much of the world.

'Burbs is the slang term for the communities that appear around the cities and strong-holds of the Coalition States, particularly around the great, fortified super-cities like Chi-Town. However, this is most definitely *not* suburbia as we think of it, but rather a collection of a ragtag people who either share the dream of becoming CS citizens inside one of the fortress cities or believe that the 'Burbs, as unstable as they may be, are safer and better than making a go of it in the wilderness or a rural community.

The first 'Burbs appeared as campsites scattered around the outer walls of the fortified city of Chi-Town. These camps were originally supposed to be a temporary *holding zone* for human refugees who sought citizenship in the Coalition States, and/or petitioned for work or residence in Chi-Town. However, peasants, farmers, woodsmen and wilderness folk throughout North America came in droves. Unable and unwilling to accommodate everybody, the local CS officials were forced to push the multitudes a safe distance beyond its city limits. With nowhere else to go, and clinging to hope that the fortress city would accept them, they pitched tents and waited.

As time passed, some turned their vehicles into homes, or built a little fence around a pitched tent. Others began to cobble together a shack or simple cabin out of wood, clay, stone and/or salvaged sheet metal, plastic and scrap. Vegetable gardens were grown to help feed those who waited. Traveling merchants stopped to hawk their wares, and some established semi-permanent trading posts. The Coalition government ignored these

"temporary camps" even as many of them grew into squatter homesteads and shanty towns. Before the CS knew it, the great city of Chi-Town was surrounded by tens of thousands of people unwilling to leave, and patiently waiting to be recognized and accepted into the city.

In the early days, the Coalition Military would forcibly remove the squatters, sometimes escorting them hundreds of miles away, but many would return after a few weeks, joined by other hopeful newcomers, to rebuild.

No matter how many times the people would be routed and the shanty towns leveled, they would return. Legends among anti-Coalition factions (the Federation of Magic and Tolkeen among them) *claim* there were instances in the early days when the great city would dispatch troops to mow down people by the thousands, bulldozing the bodies and the tents and huts and dumping them in a giant pit. (Indeed, the skeletal remains of hundreds, if not thousands were accidently unearthed among debris estimated to be at least 90-120 years old beneath one section of Ironforge. The CS claims they are the remains of early Chi-Town citizens who perished at the hands of D-Bee invaders. Nobody knows the truth, but the CS has a long history of fighting to preserve humanity and has always tried to avoid killing their own kind, at least when they embrace the Chi-Town way of life. So while most of the "Burbies" may have been crude, uneducated, and unskilled, they were *human*, making mass murder an unlikely option.) Even if the horrid tale is true, it made little difference, for still they came pleading for mercy, protection and citizenship in the fortress city. To complicate matters, at least a third of those who came really were desirable candidates for citizenship or work in Chi-Town. However, sorting through the mass of humanity thronging outside was difficult and time consuming. All that could be done was to place everyone, the desirable and the undesirable, on a *waiting list* and made to languish outside the fortified walls to fend for themselves until each applicant could be interviewed and ranked as qualified or rejected. One might think that processing these hopeful people would send them packing when rejected, which two-thirds were, but that didn't happen. At least half of those rejected stayed. Some stayed because they planned to reapply and prove themselves worthy. Others stayed so their children would have a chance of making it inside the paradise of the fortress city, while others stayed because they didn't know where else to go. After years of trying to deal with these squatters, Chi-Town (and the Coalition States government that followed) gave up and simply allowed the shanty towns to flourish, "like weeds outside the garden," as General Cabot once commented.

Over the generations, thousands of hopeful "Burbies" waiting in the slums and tent villages around the city turned into hundreds of thousands, and then millions. Over the decades, tents and shacks turned into villages, shanty towns and even modern looking cities. These communities have their own quasi-democratic republic system of government, with their own leaders and representatives, merchants' associations, commercial guidelines, laws and police force. Most are based on or inspired by the government and society they dream of someday being accepted into, the Coalition States. Many believe they will earn a place in the fortified cities *if* they can prove themselves to be "cultured," "civilized" and "worthy." They do this by adopting the ways and laws of the CS fortress cities, collaborating with CS authorities, and even by joining the Coalition Army – the latter is something Emperor Prosek took advantage of to raise an army against Tolkeen by offering preferential status and "first look" consideration of any Burbie who voluntarily joined the military to fight on the Coalition States' behalf. Over half a million joined and fought as front-line troops (and an estimated 50-65% perished on the field of combat). Afraid to leave for fear that they would be forgotten, the multitude of hopeful people pitch camp and *wait*. Since the wait may be years, they usually gather in family clans, build some sort of hut or house or live out of tents or vehicles and wait. And wait, and wait. Thus, the 'Burbs were born.

Today, the average wait for a *highly desirable* candidate to be admitted into a fortress city is 5-10 years! For the less desirable, unskilled, and uncouth masses, that wait is said to be 15-30, but few have any real chance of acceptance at all. People continue to come, apply and wait.

All 'Burbs *start* as shanty towns and tent cities, but the oldest look like full blown cities. Around *Chi-Town* they are an array of small, independent communities that flow seamlessly from one into another. Often the only elements differentiating these *unofficial* towns and neighborhoods from one another are each community's level of poverty, technology, and lawlessness or civility.

In a way, the 'Burbs can be thought of as the rings of a tree. At the *core* is a fortified city, like Chi-Town. The first several small rings of growth around the core are the oldest suburbs of the city – the first camps and shanty towns that have grown up around the city into thriving communities in their own right. Around the center and the inner core that is the *Old Towns* are the larger *New Town 'Burbs* followed by the equally large and newest *Shanty Town 'Burbs*. Chi-Town has some of the oldest and largest 'Burbs of all the allied States – Free Quebec and Iron Heart are next in line. This is because most refugees are attracted to the largest, most prosperous and famous of the fortress cities.

The Coalition way is the best way. Since the vast majority of those living in the 'Burbs dream of one day being chosen to live in the great fortified city of Chi-Town or one of the other fortified cities in the States, most humans believe in and try to live by many, if not all, of the laws and views of the Coalition Government in general and Chi-Town in particular. To win favor and acceptance, many of the squatter communities zealously practice and preach what they see as the *Coalition way*. This means most are human supremacists who are suspicious and fearful of non-humans, if not outright hateful of them. Many outspokenly chastise and rebuke nonhumans, and threaten, mistreat and attack D-Bees, dragons, and other nonhumans with little or no provocation. They also feed on CS propaganda, accepting it as gospel and doing whatever the Emperor or CS authorities might ask of them. This is especially true in the *oldest* and (arguably) most "civilized" and established *Old Town 'Burbs*. Consequently, the 'Burbs present the CS with thousands of willing spies, informers and sympathizers willing to rat-out their neighbors and visitors to make a name for themselves and hopefully earn the Coalition's favor to get bumped higher up on the waiting list of citizenship in Chi-Town. The CS exploits this "hope" mercilessly.

That having been said, there are people who have opposing views and question, challenge and/or defy the *Coalition way*. Most of these folks are inhabitants of the New Towns and new arrivals to Shanty Towns, or visiting adventurers and outsiders. However, those who have opposing views or engage in illegal activities must be very careful in exactly how they express themselves and to whom they talk. CS spies, undercover cops, bounty hunters, mercenaries and civilian sympathizers are everywhere, so one never knows what kind of trouble he might elicit if he isn't careful. Likewise, criminals, rebel groups and dissidents might try to enlist, trick or extort careless visitors into working for their cause, or target the visitors for some other nefarious operation. Furthermore, "crimes" in the shadow of Chi-Town include things like owning magic items and practicing magic, possessing pre-Rifts artifacts and knowledge, possessing banned books and films, supporting and reading the works of Erin Tarn, teaching D-Bees how to read and write, being a nonhuman or helping nonhumans, and harboring dangerous thoughts, such as believing in a different way of life than the Coalition's chosen path. The latter includes thinking D-Bees should have human rights or that the use of magic is not inherently bad or evil.

Old Town 'Burbs

If there is a high society in the mostly rough and tumble 'Burbs, it is the power brokers, business people and wealthy members of the Old Town communities.

Generally speaking, the Old Town 'Burbs – the ones that look most like real, permanent modern cities and factory districts outside the fortress city – are the most dedicated and loyal to the Coalition States. They are the oldest, most established and permanent of the 'Burbs. Some are very old and have existed for 50-80 years. In fact, they are so clean and well kept that if one did not know better, they could be mistaken for genuine Coalition towns or small cities. The loyalty, admiration, and obedience of many Old Town inhabitants often borders on the fanatical. Most of the people living here are willing to do almost anything to see members of their community become residents of the fortress city. These denizens of the 'Burbs tend to be psychotic about appearing civilized, cultured and desirable to the Coalition States. That means obeying CS laws and adopting CS customs to the "T," making them the most law abiding, orderly, and zealous human supremacists living anywhere in the 'Burbs. Old Town settlements are also the safest places in the 'Burbs. At least two thirds of their structures, from businesses to residences, are permanent structures, one to four stories tall. Two thirds of the commercial buildings are Mega-Damage structures, as are a third of the homes. Likewise, half the streets are paved, the rest are covered with gravel, and only the back alleys are dirt (and half of them are covered with gravel). There is very little that changes in the Old Town 'Burbs. Businesses come and go but most of the buildings and streets stay the same. Only in the event of a destructive fire, battle, or large urban renewal project is there a major change to the size, look and shape of an Old Town 'Burb. By comparison, the buildings and streets in the New Town and Shanty Town 'Burbs are constantly changing.

The Old Town sections are "managed" by a formal, but *unofficial* seat of government, including a self-regulated judiciary and police force who follow the law of the Coalition States to the letter. Additionally, many factories and businesses in Old Town 'Burbs manufacture goods and perform services for the fortress city, and these denizens of the 'Burbs regularly enjoy day and weekend passes into the city itself!

The inhabitants of these elder 'Burbs usually consider themselves to be steadfast loyalists to the Coalition States and Emperor Prosek, and whether true or not, they choose to believe they are among the *most favored* by the CS, thus making their citizens the elite upper-crust in the 'Burbs, and therefore the most likely to become city residents; or so they have convinced themselves. As the upper-crust in 'Burb society, many turn their nose up to newcomers, poor folks, adventurers and those who criticize the CS or engage in "unsavory and criminal activities."

Unsavory and criminal activities can be a pretty long list, especially for real fanatics, but the following are typically accepted as "unsavory" by most Old Townees and a good half of the New Town folks.

- Studying, researching, teaching, believing or even just talking about pre-Rifts history that conflicts with or challenges the "official history" presented by the Coalition States.
- Collecting pre-Rifts artifacts; particularly technological secrets, weapons and books, films and video *banned* by the CS. All such artifacts are supposed to be turned over to Coalition authorities for proper evaluation and archiving.
- Selling contraband, particularly magic, alien artifacts, and the books of Erin Tarn.

- The private study and/or practice of magic is absolutely taboo even for personal use or entertainment. Those who practice and/or encourage the use of magic on any scale are typically regarded as dangerous malcontents or traitors, and ratted out to the CS.
- Collecting a few magical odds and ends, or owning a couple of books on the subject of magic, and even a magic weapon or two are seen as dangerous and forbidden. However, among the high society of the Old 'Burbs, its is increasingly tolerated, as long as the owner is very, very discreet about it and not showy or threatening. In fact, owning a few magic items has become highly fashionable and prestigious, and said to exhibit a daring and bold personality. Thus, it is "deliciously exciting and adventurous" to own 1-4 forbidden magic items in a secret collection (most are usually small, basic items). The CS is completely unaware of this growing social trend among the Old Town elite, but is not likely to care too much, because they know these 'Burbies are extremely loyal to the CS and would never use such items in acts of rebellion, insurrection or anything else. On the other hand, these wealthy and decadent elite of the 'Burb subculture sometimes acquire rare, powerful and/or dangerous magic items without any idea of what they have. This may endanger their lives if "outsiders" (particularly members of the Federation of Magic, thieves, dragons and evil mages) covet the item, or if it has a corrupting/evil effect on its owner, or endangers the lives of their family and neighbors if it could unleash a dangerous being or destructive force when improperly used.
- Dealing in alien technology – "alien" as in, out of this world, an alien race like the Naruni, Kittani or Splugorth.
- Dealing in magic, teaching magic or using magic for personal gain are heinous crimes for which there is no excuse or tolerance. Most Old Townees will turn in a neighbor without hesitation when they think they are using or trafficking in magic.
- Association or fraternization with the Federation of Magic (seen as a mortal enemy of Chi-Town and the Coalition States for generations) is an act of treason and villainy beyond redemption and is immediately reported to Coalition authorities (or dealt with quietly within the power structure of the 'Burbs themselves).
- Association or fraternization with demons and monsters (i.e., dragons, Splugorth and their minions, and other creatures of magic and supernatural beings), and often extends to Shifters, Witches and Necromancers. This is an act of treason and villainy punishable by death.
- Words (and actions) of insurrection. It *is* okay to complain and criticize the Coalition States, its Emperor, the Prosek family and especially policies concerning the 'Burbs and citizenship, however, it is quite another thing to promote rebellion, civil unrest, riots, overturning the government or physical attacks on the CS police, military or government.
- Most *conventional* crimes are handled by the "local" 'Burbs authorities or private individuals.

Note: Whenever its says something is immediately "reported" to Coalition authorities, it means this act is seen as a terrible and dangerous crime that threatens the stability of human civilization, and is probably treasonous and of the utmost importance. *However*, it may not actually get reported to Coalition authorities. As good as their relationship is with Chi-Town and the Coalition Army, police and politicians, even Old Town 'Burbs can be invaded, purged, and obliterated by Coalition forces as easily as the Shanty and New Towns, especially if the authorities fear that the community harbors dangerous dissidents or represents a serious threat to Chi-Town security. As a result, serious problems involving magic, aliens, monsters, forbidden teachings, and acts of insurrection and treason are frequently (90% of the time) dealt with "internally" by the powers that be within the Old Town 'Burbs themselves. Each of the Old Towns has its own political structure, leaders, police force, independent protectors and powerful individuals who see to such "delicate matters." Their philosophy is, why involve the CS and make them nervous or suspicious when they can handle the matter themselves, without Coalition knowledge or involvement? This is a constant when it comes to the Old Towns, with each working in concert to quietly eliminate such sources of trouble amongst themselves. However Old Town politics and justice often overflows into the New Towns and Shanty Towns. The old guard often see these places as nothing but troublesome dens of iniquity inhabited by uncouth rabble, thieves, wild men and nonhumans, in the first place, so they have no qualms about taking independent action to solve things *they* see as problems, circumventing the local law and leadership to quiet things down or further their own agendas. Consequently, the leaders, wealthy and powerful members of the Old Towns are constantly sticking their noses into the affairs of the New and Shanty Town 'Burbs, often stirring the pot and creating as much trouble as they resolve. This may involve hiring mercenaries, assassins, adventurers or criminals, or using a "trusted insider" (a citizen or friend of an Old Town) to assassinate, sabotage, frame, intimidate, extort or do whatever else may be deemed necessary for "the greater good of everyone" – or so the most arrogant of the Old Town elite see it that way. The local powers don't appreciate the Old Townees' warnings, interference and direct intervention, all of which creates a strong sense of "them and us" and the notion that the Old Townees are the lap dogs of the CS and possibly even Coalition spies, assassins and secret agents. Along those same lines, while the leadership of the Old Towns quietly work together to solve problems without involving the CS, they have no qualms about informing on "suspicious or illegal" activity, people and places in the other "uncivilized 'Burbs."

Typical Statistical Breakdowns for Most Old Town 'Burbs:

92-98% Human population.

2.5% Psi-Stalkers (human mutants).

1-3.5% D-Bees and others (unwanted refugees, supernatural beings and creatures of magic). The exceptions are towns with heavy industry where 4-6% of the population may be D-Bee slaves or forced labor and kept very quiet.

91% are dedicated human supremacists.

87% have nothing to do with D-Bees whatsoever, and shun them completely.

1-4% accept magic in any form; all others (96-99%) fear and reject it. None practice it openly.

5-15% are literate in American. (**Note:** The Chi-Town 'Burbs are an exception because they are so old.)

4% Possess psychic abilities; 99% of those are IC registered psychics with Psi-Net.

10% of the buildings are tents, huts, shacks and vehicles turned into dwellings.

50% are 1-10 story buildings (average is four story); half are M.D.C. structures. The rest are small homes.

75% of the Old Town 'Burb is permanent and mostly unchanging. Streets and businesses are well established and don't change or move much.

Crime is low.

Poverty is low, only about 20% are truly poor. The rest live well and may be considered middle class, while 10% are downright well-to-do and 5% (mostly criminal kingpins and merchants) are worth millions of credits.

Has a solid and strong local governing body and militia/police, but may also have a few street or criminal gangs as well as powerful and influential businesses and individuals.

CS authorities have the most trust and respect for the Old Town 'Burbs and regularly go to its local governing body to resolve any problems before resorting to violence. Soldiers sweep the Old Town 'Burbs only once or twice a week, although there may be an increase if trouble is afoot or if the 'Burb's leaders call the CS in to resolve a problem; namely incidents involving spies, terrorists with a vendetta against the CS, rebel dissidents, practitioners of magic, and those speaking out against Emperor Prosek and/or spreading history and propaganda contrary to the Coalition's views. It may also be visited by the police from the fortress city, but only if it is suspected that the culprits of a crime or trouble are hiding in an Old Town, or the police are looking for the help of Old Town authorities to track down a suspect or criminal operation in one of the other 'Burbs.

New Town 'Burbs

The newer, but established 'Burbs are known as **New Town 'Burbs**. They are larger, more sprawling than the Old Towns and are seldom more than 7-10 years old, falling prey to destruction and CS purges only to be rebuilt as someplace new. New Towns are unstructured, disorganized and only partially civilized. They are noisy communities with gravel and mud streets, poor sanitation and a haphazard layout. The only semi-permanent structures are the 2-5 story buildings of its business district, filled with trading posts, saloons, boarding houses, entertainment and places of ill-repute. The business area is surrounded by small homes, shacks, broken down vehicles used for housing, tents and campsites. Only twenty percent are Mega-Damage structures. Most of these New Towns are consid-

ered to be established communities and function as towns or small cities in and of themselves, complete with their own local government and police force. Like the Old Towns, most 'Burb governments are patterned on the Coalition States or the idea of a democratic republic, though some, like Razor Ridge, are dictatorships and others more like a feudal kingdom.

The atmosphere is similar to the boomtowns of the pre-Rifts American Wild West, where there are shootouts in the streets, the community never seems to sleep, and there is always something going on (whether one wants it to or not). These are the communities where organized crime and the Black Market abound, and where one can find just about whatever illegal substance, pleasure or information he may be looking for. Of course, the Coalition Military patrols these places regularly and frequently sets up "sting" operations to capture criminals and spies. Bounty hunters, mercenaries, slavers, scholars, psychics, practitioners of magic, Juicers, Crazies, 'Borgs, City Rats, adventurers, D-Bees and monsters also call the New Town 'Burbs home, or use them as a rest stop to resupply and have a little fun, or to get lost in a sea of faces, human and inhuman.

Unsavory and illegal activity is commonplace at most New Towns; the crime rate is moderate to high, at least in parts of town. In most cases, half to two thirds of the inhabitants are (mostly) Coalition loyalists and Chi-Town wannabes, however, a third to half are resigned to spending the rest of their lives in the 'Burbs and do whatever it takes to survive. These pragmatists are also the most likely to question, criticize and speak out against the CS, its laws, leaders, police and military, as well as read (many practically worship) the books and words of Erin Tarn, study alternative theories of history (other than the official CS propaganda), accept D-Bees (as second-class citizens if not full 50/50 equals), and even accept (if not actually practice) magic. In fact, even some of the loyalists question the Coalition States' harsh stance on magic or the collecting and studying of ancient, pre-Rifts artifacts, books, films and culture. (Of course, the reason is simple, the CS doesn't want its people to learn about old Earth cultures' battles for democracy, civil rights, and equality for all people for fear it may lead to discontent, weaken its power base and challenge the currently widely accepted dictatorial culture. It's all about maintaining the status quo by keeping the people ignorant but blissful.) As a result, the New Towns are the places to go to find banned books, magic items, illegal technology like Juicer and Crazy conversions, Body-Chop-Shops, illegal weapons and other contraband. Likewise, this is where one can find magical and psychic healing, mercenaries and adventurers for hire, Rogue Scholars, Rogue Scientists, Operator mechanics' garages, smugglers, the Black Market, D-Bees and a fairly large range of entertainment from family fare to the decadent.

Among the residents are people who have traveled and seen the world (or at least the continent) and who may still have connections to the outside world or hide away some alien or magical artifact. These worldly inhabitants are retired and semi-retired men at arms, mercenaries, explorers, Rogue Scientists, Rogue Scholars, Psi-Stalkers, adventurers and other travelers.

Unlike the Old Towns which tend to close themselves off from the outside world, the New Towns offer goods and services that attract outsiders, so there is always a constant stream of adventurers, men at arms, Psi-Stalkers, merchants, farmers, refugees, D-Bees and even practitioners of magic, dragons and other alien, magical or supernatural beings (the latter usually in disguise) in town. Farmers and crafts people come to sell and trade their wares, as do trappers and Wilderness Scouts, adventurers and warriors come to sell or trade the booty of war or just to get a little rest and relaxation before going back out into the world. Bounty hunters and cutthroats may come to collect on a bounty or seeking the target of a bounty, or just to get a drink or resupply. In many regards, the New Town 'Burbs, more than any other, are centers of commerce. They're places to buy and sell goods or services, to resupply, rest, hide, spend money or acquire any number of different modern conveniences, tools, weapons or contraband. And because so many "outsiders" come and go, also centers for news, rumors, gossip, and the buying, selling and trade of information and secrets. In fact, this constant exchange of information is what makes the New Town 'Burbs less inclined to buy into the Coalition's propaganda and compels them to consider other viewpoints and ideas. The high level of traffic in and out also makes the New Towns perfect for smuggling and for passing secrets and contraband. All of these factors are what compel the CS to maintain such a constant military and police presence (as well as spies and undercover agents) in the New Town 'Burbs, launching purges to shake things up, ferret out spies, mages and undesirables, and to break down criminal networks, smuggling rings and dissidents before they get too entrenched or powerful.

Note: Unlike the Old Town 'Burbs, even steadfast loyalists hesitate to "report" activity or trouble that might instigate a Coalition purge or any kind of disruptive CS intervention or shakedown. This means they tend to report isolated incidents, minor trouble and conventional crime which the CS authorities may or may not take an interest in. The human supremacists of New Towns are also quick to finger D-Bee crooks, scoundrels, and innocent passers-by for crimes and trouble even when they may not be responsible for it. Of course, CS authorities are quick to act on any accusations against D-Bees, dragons, monsters and practitioners of magic. However, because incidents involving forbidden knowledge (including magic and pre-Rifts books, films and artifacts) often result in an overblown and destructive CS response, most New Town inhabitants ignore them or keep quiet. So what if a bunch of two-bit dissidents, Rogue Scholars, Scientists or Tarn advocates are secretly teaching kids to read or smuggling and selling old books and artifacts, or Erin Tarn titles? Let 'em. Who is it hurting? Loyalists dismiss all that sort of stuff as lies and tripe anyway. Likewise, the discreet use, study and teaching of magic as well as the quiet sale of magic items and alien gadgets are usually ignored, though these activities are much more unacceptable and frightening, so if things heat up or get too scary, the CS or local authorities *are* notified.

Speaking of local authorities, New Town police, vigilantes, influential business people and powerful individuals frequently try to step in and quell any trouble and activities that might bring the Coalition Army or police down on them. In fact, the local police and hired guns often find themselves in a race to bring down trouble and conceal the true extent of the operation or cover up the incident before Coalition forces find out or arrive on the scene. For this reason, the CS rarely trusts the local authorities, and the local authorities have become expert spin-doctors to weave convincing cover stories that the CS can't

prove otherwise even if they suspect a cover up. And because the CS is so extreme in its handling of situations with practitioners of magic, D-Bees, supernatural beings, and treason, many citizens willingly jump in to help cover-up the truth, provided the local authorities or their hired adventurers have *truly* stopped the villains and have this situation well under control.

Ironically, the Coalition's own disdain and attitude contributes to the *lack* of trust and cooperation from inhabitants of the New Town 'Burbs, and works to help make cover ups easy. After all, the majority of the Coalition authorities, police and military personnel don't care if the inhabitants of the 'Burbs kill each other, die from disease, enslave and mistreat D-Bees, struggle against supernatural predators or destroy themselves in any way, provided their internal conflicts and behavior do not *directly affect* or threaten the security of the Coalition States or the human citizens of Chi-Town (or whatever CS fortress city may be nearby). A Coalition Grunt or ISS police officer will step over the body of a dead D-Bee without so much as a, "what happened here?" The body of a monster or demon *may* elicit an investigation to make sure there aren't *more* lurking around or building an army of worshipers or minions that might threaten the citizens of the neighboring CS communities. The body of a human is more likely to raise an eyebrow, provided the deceased is not a known vagabond, gang member, City Rat, criminal or troublemaker (i.e., somebody who spoke against the CS or the Emperor). The murder of a respected citizen from the fortress city who foolishly *visited a 'Burb*, even if he was a known scoundrel involved in criminal or morally reprehensible activities, always warrants a thorough investigation, however, and may be reason for a "shakedown," "purge" or "culling."

17

Even when the 'Burbs are *not* under martial law, both the Coalition Military and ISS maintain a presence via frequent patrols, investigations and shakedowns.

Shakedowns are surprise raids to "flush some of the rats into the open and see what we get." Such raids are typically directed at Rogue Scholars and Scientists, practitioners of magic, nonhumans and organized crime, particularly brazen Black Market operations.

Purges are full military invasions that can devastate entire neighborhoods, see the slaughter of dozens, the imprisonment and/or routing of hundreds and, occasionally, the obliteration of some or all of that 'Burb.

Cullings are similar to shakedowns and purges, but with the express purpose of cutting out and removing – culling them from the rest of "the herd" within the 'Burbs – a specific faction of people; i.e. practitioners of magic, psychics, a particular gang, monsters or D-Bees. A culling may start with one specific type/creature in mind, but generally degenerates to include everybody who falls into that broad category. Anybody who opposes the action or gets in the way is rolled over, and probably killed.

Statistical Breakdown & Notes Common to New Town 'Burbs:

70-84% human population.

5-8% Psi-Stalkers (mutant humans).

6-20% D-Bees, occasionally more. Most D-Bees are illegal slaves, indentured servants, or renegades on the run and living the low life. Independent and visiting D-Bees are typically adventurers, Rogue Scholars, Rogue Scientists, Bounty Hunters, Mercenaries, Vagabonds and traders. The CS considers all D-Bees to be untrustworthy miscreants, but corrupt soldiers and police often ignore D-Bees kept as slaves and servants unless they act suspicious or cause trouble. D-Bees who cause trouble or commit a crime – even a minor offense – are savagely brutalized and often killed on the spot; no arrest nor trial is necessary. D-Bees have no rights. Consequently, D-Bees who are only accused of a crime or wanted for questioning run for their lives and hide from the authorities. Independent, free D-Bees are considered to be spies, assassins, the worst kinds of criminals or dangerous rebels out to undermine and destroy the Coalition States. As such, they are automatically wanted for "questioning and extermination!" Lazy CS soldiers and police often give up the chase for D-Bee suspects who prove to be too elusive, difficult or dangerous to pursue, while corrupt ones may accept bribes and payoffs to look the other way and let D-Bees go or even arrange their escape from local 'Burb authorities and lynch mobs.

1-2% others; unwanted supernatural beings and creatures of magic.

50-60% are dedicated human supremacists.

40% have nothing to do with D-Bees whatsoever and shun them completely.

4-10% practice magic! You read that correctly, as many as 10% of a 'Burb's inhabitants may practice or otherwise embrace magic (use TW weapons and devices, or magic weapons, deal in magic, etc.)

40% fear but accept magic as a strange but useful ability; they look the other way to its practice, especially if the magic is used to their benefit.

50% fear and shun magic, and will turn those who practice it or shelter magic users over to the authorities.

2-6% are literate in American; this percentage may be double or triple in progressive and wealthy 'Burbs.

6-12% possess some measure of psychic abilities.

30-50% of all buildings and homes are tents, shacks, huts and vehicles turned into dwellings or trading posts.

25% are 2-5 story buildings; half are businesses and half are M.D.C. structures which can be considered semi-permanent structures. Only a few of the most traveled streets (namely the business area) are permanent. Otherwise the configuration of the streets, buildings and houses change regularly; every few (2D4) weeks.

25% are 1-2 story homes; one third are M.D.C. structures.

Crime is moderate to high. Poverty is the norm. Only 20-30% live well, 3-6% high on the hog. Note that by CS standards, crime is rampant, because they consider reading forbidden books and using magic as a "crime."

There *is* a local governing body, police force and neighborhood militia, but depending on the 'Burb and changing times, it may be a vocal and showy figurehead, corrupt or criminal authority and alternately, a true and honest governing body. Most New Town 'Burbs also have *at least* half a dozen street and criminal gangs as well as some influential merchants and powerful individuals.

The Coalition Army sends soldiers to patrol the streets of a New Town 'Burb 1D4+4 times a day, and may also conduct 1D4+1 flybys (usually rocket bikes, Sky-Cycles or SAMAS). It may also be patrolled or visited by the police from the fortress city (ISS or NTSET), but only if it's suspected that the culprits of a crime or trouble are hiding or based in the 'Burb.

New Towns are perfect for spies and undercover police officers (namely the ISS). However, there are much fewer CS undercover and spy operations going on than most people imagine. The CS has a few long-term operations in place, and may send spies out when they suspect something big or important is going down, but otherwise could care less about the goings on in the 'Burbs. The Chi-Town Department of Internal Security and the Coalition Army concur that Chi-Town defenses and security measures are the best there is, and that the city is virtually impregnable with layers of redundancy measures in place to catch anyone (or anything) that manages to slip through.

The Tolkeen situation has caused Chi-Town to increase the number of patrols and spies in the 'Burbs and in the fortress city to counter any acts of retribution by Tolkeen survivors and sympathizers. Attention on the 'Burbs, particularly the New Towns, is also intended to intercept dangerous magic and contraband items, as well as war criminals and dissident who are like to make their way to the cities.

Shanty Towns

The outer ring of tent villages, muddy compounds and vehicle parks are Shanty Town 'Burbs, the latest gatherings of the hopeful and visitors. Shanty Towns are just what they sound like, and are the poorest, most wild, lawless and deplorable of the 'Burbs. Shanty Towns are the largest, most sprawling and least organized of the three types of 'Burbs. A third are transients who won't stay for more than a month or two, though there are always newcomers to take their place. The 'Burb itself has few actual buildings except maybe a couple of trading posts and/or a town hall for meetings and gatherings. Nor do the Shanty Towns have much in the way of stores and shops, as most people travel to the New Towns to buy supplies, sell their wares or find entertainment and work. The majority of Shanty Towns are divided up into sections ruled by gangs, criminal organizations or powerful individuals (Juicers, 'Borgs, psychics, practitioners of magic, merchants, etc., good and evil). Some are even controlled by monsters lurking in the shadows where they pull the strings of their human puppets. Since there are no formal laws or official ruling body, anarchy prevails and the level of violence, crime, corruption and mayhem can change dramatically from one Shanty Town neighborhood to the next – often without warning. Most Shanty Town 'Burbs are considered sprawling, lawless dens of iniquity where visitors can purchase all kinds of low-end contraband and lose themselves among the masses. Thus, they are havens for fugitives, runaway slaves, bandits, thieves, practitioners of magic, D-Bees, monsters, spies, and adventurers, as well as terrorists and enemies of the Coalition States.

The smallest Shanty Towns are little more than a gathering of strangers and nomads. Most of these "little villages" are composed of tents and ramshackle buildings made from scraps and the gutted husks of vehicles. These can have as few as 20-100 people and are the most likely to be temporary dwelling places that fall victim to roaming gangs, thugs, monsters, disease, or the Coalition Military. These places never have large, permanent structures nor attract merchants, although small time merchants selling items from the trunk of their vehicle, smugglers, traveling shows, adventurers and mercenaries with booty to sell,

trapper/woodsmen, Cyber-Docs or con men may temporarily set up shop.

Because there are no tall buildings nor organization, most Shanty Town 'Burbs are sprawling affairs that rather resemble a tent city, refugee camp or the packed parking lot of a massive pre-Rifts stadium for a major sporting event – with vehicles, tents, campsites and people going every which way for miles and miles. For most visitors, one only passes through or goes around a Shanty Town (they are kept away from the main roads to Chi-Town). Shanty Towns are worse than slums, conditions are deplorable, and sanitation is a nightmare.

Average Statistical Breakdown & Notes for Shanty Town 'Burbs:

60-75% human population.

15-20% D-Bees; most of which (70%) are independent and free adventurers, mercenaries, Vagabonds, Rogue Scholars and Rogue Scientists, and other O.C.C.s and R.C.C.s. 30% are slaves and indentured servants. The general situation with D-Bees and how the CS responds to them is basically the same as described under *New Town 'Burbs.*

10-15% Psi-Stalkers (mutant humans).

2-5% others; supernatural beings and creatures of magic.

35% are dedicated human supremacists.

40% have nothing to do with D-Bees whatsoever and shun them completely.

1-4% are literate in American.

10-15% accept and practice magic!

40-50% fear but accept magic as a strange but useful ability; they look the other way to its practice, especially if magic is used to their benefit.

30% fear and shun magic, and will turn in those who practice it or shelter magic users.

20-30% don't know what to think about magic.

8-15% possess some sort of psychic abilities.

95% are tents, huts, shacks & vehicles turned into dwellings.

5% are one and two story buildings; half are M.D.C. structures. *None* can be considered permanent. The configuration of the mud and dirt streets, buildings and houses move and change regularly (every 4D6 days), with people, businesses and places appearing, moving or disappearing completely, replaced by somebody new.

Crime is rampant. Poverty, lawlessness and uncertainty reign.

There is no governing body or authority other than rival gangs, powerful individuals and CS military patrols who wander the Shanty Town 'Burb 2D4+8 times a day. It may also be patrolled or visited by the police from the fortress city, but only if the 'Burb is suspected of harboring culprits responsible for crimes or troubles in the city.

Shanty Town 'Burbs are investigated and tossed by the CS authorities, military and police, every few days, and they are likely to knock apart 2D4x10% of it every month or two. Whenever the CS troops want to make an example of someone, D-Bees or practitioners of magic and those known or suspected of associating with either group are targeted (and usually killed in the streets).

Note: Since the Shanty Town 'Burbs are inhabited by the poorest and newest arrivals, 60-75% of the people are as green, uneducated, unskilled and unsophisticated as they come, making them easy victims to con artists and easily frightened, angered and turned into a mob. However, because they are dirt-poor, most crimes are small time or born from passion. Big time crooks and adventurers have no interest in Shanty Towns unless it is to find somebody hiding in them or they are looking for cheap labor or to stir up trouble.

For more information on the 'Burbs and how the CS sees them, as well as CS police and military actions in the 'Burbs, see **Rifts® World Book 11: Coalition War Campaign.** Also, the **Rifts® Adventure Guide** offers more info on the 'Burbs, plus 50 adventure ideas, while the **Rifts® Bionics Sourcebook** presents several varieties of City Rats and the villainous Cyber-Snatcher, as well as data and info on Cyber-Docs, Body-Chop-Shops, cybernetic systems and bionics all gathered in one book.

Forbidden Knowledge

Despite their power, the leaders of Chi-Town and the Coalition States fear many things. One is magic. Another is free thought. And another is opposing views and different ways of life.

Note: Some people mistakenly believe the CS fears D-Bees, but that is not true. They wage a campaign of hate to mislead their citizens into fearing nonhumans because it gives them a common enemy – a demon to galvanize the people and get them to trust and turn to their government for protection and guidance. That trust, in turn, gives the Prosek regime incredible amounts of power in the name of national security, defense, justice and freedom. It is a brilliant and effective ruse Emperor Prosek has exploited to the maximum for years now, and in the process has made himself, the government, and the Coalition Army the saviors of human civilization.

This plot has led the CS to forbid, condemn and ban 1) magic in all its forms, 2) the writings and speeches of Erin Tarn (the lady, herself, branded as a criminal and dangerous traitor), 3) books from *before* the Coming of the Rifts (and literacy in general), 4) old films/movies and television, 5) alien technology, and 6) anything that challenges or goes against Coalition teachings or its way of thinking, and that last one is a pretty broad category.

Magic

Nothing has been more maligned and vilified than magic and those who wield its secrets. According to Coalition propaganda hammered and hammered into the heads of its citizens, magic is inherently evil – a mysterious power said to be drawn from vile, demonic beings who seek to torture, enslave and destroy humankind. A sinister force that blackens the soul and twists the

mind. As evidence of magic's evil and destructive nature, the CS points a condemning finger to its favorite bogie-man, the Federation of Magic – the poster child for dark magic, demonic forces and evil, all directed at Chi-Town. Exaggerated and one-sided versions of the War on Tolkeen and other incidents involving practitioners of magic out to harm Chi-Town and humans only help to convince those living isolated within the Coalition States to believe the worst and shun magic in all its forms. This nonstop propaganda campaign has worked so well that most citizens of the Coalition States are terrified of magic and report the mere suspicion of magic use in a heartbeat – at least in the fortress cities and other large communities of the States.

Things are different in the 'Burbs. Perhaps it is because the 'Burbs exist in that limbo state outside the parameters of CS society, and because its residents have much greater contact with the rest of the world (including practitioners of magic), that magic is seen through different eyes. Though Coalition forces condemn and outlaw magic in the 'Burbs, actively seeking it out for elimination, magic is not seen as the great evil by the people who live there. Many in the 'Burbs have seen magic work wonders and save lives, thus, about half of those in the New Towns and Shanty Towns accept magic as having value, and while they do not embrace its use, they don't condemn it either. Consequently, most Burbies turn a blind eye toward practitioners of magic, the sale and distribution of magic items, and even the use of magic as long as it is to the benefit of the 'Burbs' inhabitants. That having been said, there is no love for the Federation of Magic. The Federation has caused too much grief and bloodshed to ever be trusted completely, so anybody who comes from the Federation of Magic is presumed to be up to no good and viewed as evil and dangerous until proven otherwise. Even then, there are those who will never trust a Federation sorcerer. Likewise, Necromancers, Witches, Shifters and others who consort with demons, the dead and the supernatural are looked upon with fear and revulsion. Still, if one keeps to himself and stays out of trouble, most people will ignore practitioners of magic and leave them to conduct whatever business they may have in the 'Burbs; this is especially true of New Town 'Burbs and Shanty Towns.

Even those Burbies who avoid magic often question how it can be inherently evil, especially when they see what good it can do and hear about spell casters who are good and heroic. As a result, there is a growing portion of Burbies who will seek the counsel of a mage, turn to practitioners of magic for healing and other magical help, and/or use a magic item. Techno-Wizardry is the most readily accepted, probably because its technological machines and devices seem familiar and their use doesn't actually require any knowledge of magic, making the seem like most any other high-tech machine. Of course, those who do use Techno-Wizard items do so quietly, for fear of getting caught by Coalition forces. It is illegal to own, use or trade magic in any form, including Techno-Wizard devices, and those caught with one or more in their possession see the item seized or destroyed and they are beaten, interrogated (which often means torture), fined, imprisoned or killed, sometimes right on the spot. Those who flee or try to fight Coalition authorities are pursued and gunned down in the street. Worse, friends, family and associates are likely to be questioned, frisked for illegal contraband and possibly taken into custody for further interrogation or killed where they are found as conspirators in the *trafficking of magic.* The CS has zero tolerance for magic and their tactics are as extreme as they come. **Note:** This gives corrupt and overzealous Coalition forces considerable power, because all they have to say is they had reason to believe an individual was a practitioner of magic, using magical devices and/or teaching, hiding or selling magic. Nobody questions if one or a hundred D-Bees are killed under this pretext, nor if some no name adventurer meets his end this way. However, if the target is a notable resident of the 'Burbs, CS authorities need to be a bit more careful. They have ultimate power and jurisdiction over everybody in the 'Burbs, but if they hope to avoid riots, street retribution, or further difficulties, they need to have good cause and genuine proof.

The works of Erin Tarn

Erin Tarn is the most famous and beloved Rogue Scholar in North America and a constant source of consternation to Emperor Prosek and the Coalition States. Her courage, conviction and honest words combined with the Coalition's lasting persecution have made her a folk hero. Even many of the people who don't believe what she has to say (choosing to believe CS propaganda for whatever reason) grudgingly respect her. In the New Town 'Burbs and communities outside the CS, Erin Tarn is a celebrity and a living legend, with countless numbers of people willing to help her or pass along her words. Though most people on Rifts Earth are illiterate, Erin Tarn's books are printed and distributed by the thousands, with a hundred times that number

in *audio book* form for listening use in computers and disk players. Furthermore, those who can read, do so aloud for audiences as few as a single youngster to dozens, hundreds and even gatherings of thousands.

Anything and everything attributed to Erin Tarn is illegal and banned in the Coalition States. Anyone caught with one of her works is beaten and the article confiscated and destroyed. Mass market sellers are executed as rebels and the books or disks destroyed, often on the spot. Anyone found to have harbored the famous historian is considered a traitor and may be executed as such, not that it stops most people from doing so. **Note:** The works of Erin Tarn are so common, particularly among visitors to the 'Burbs and the inhabitants of New Towns, that the Coalition forces who patrol the streets confiscate and destroy the item, threaten and beat the individual in possession of it, and move on as a matter of routine. Corrupt authorities (CS police and soldiers) may also "fine" the individual, taking (for themselves) credits and/or belongings they find desirable or which they can sell on the street or to the Black Market. People who "refuse to cooperate" are beaten severely or killed and stripped of all (or most) of their belongings. Any Burbie or visitor who reports such acts of misconduct can expect similar retribution by other corrupt officers assigned to the 'Burbs, or even legitimate Coalition officers who either don't believe the allegations or don't like their "good name" being smeared by a bunch of D-Bees, troublemaking outsiders or tattletales.

Books & Literacy

Though not strictly forbidden, the CS frowns upon formal education and *literacy* for the masses. It prefers to keep the majority of its people ignorant and unable to read so it can spoon feed them whatever it wants through spoken and visual presentations on television, radio and pictures. Except among the upper echelon, *everything* in the Coalition States is visual and audio. Even the Coalition States' internet is primarily made up of icons, symbols, pictures and audio-visual presentations of data rather than words. Likewise, street signs and warnings are all *icon based,* displaying a visual image that represent "X" rather than a word. Stores flash picture images and logo designs with lights, and the blare of music, slogans, and spoken announcements, advertisements and pitches emit from speakers everywhere. The concept is that if the majority of people cannot read, then they can't be as easily influenced by outside forces and different (corrupting) ideas. Isolating the people inside a fortified paradise where they and their families are safe, and the written word is not important, helps to enforce their goal of 90% illiteracy.

Surprisingly few people realize this is a deliberate plan on the part of the Coalition government, or don't believe it. Most CS citizens content with their lives don't miss the written word nor do they see anything wrong with being illiterate. After all, they don't need books and writing when all the news and entertainment they can get is on the television, radio and regional internet – and all presented in a slick, entertaining way via sound and visuals.

Ironically, Burbies waiting for citizenship to a Coalition fortress city don't realize that if they can read, it is an *automatic disqualification* for eligibility. The only exceptions are if, for some reason, the candidate is considered highly desirable or there are mitigating circumstances to allow citizenship to a "Reader." From the Coalition's paranoid point of view, literacy is like a hereditary disease. If the parents have it, they will probably pass it along to their children, and the disease of literacy may also be spread to friends and acquaintances, and the CS wouldn't want that now, would they?

This is why *Rogue Scholars* and *Rogue Scientists* are branded as criminals, dissidents, traitors and madmen – they are contaminated with an open mind and their world view corrupted by different cultures and ideas. They have had, through reading, experienced many different ideas, events and concepts. They have a different understanding of life and a larger view of the world. All of that makes them question the status quo and want to learn new things and uncover more knowledge, history and truth. Things the Coalition States discourages. The CS wants happy, complacent sheep, not explorers and philosophers. Education, reading and creative thought are reserved for the educated elite who hold positions of power within the Coalition government and business world (and even many top business people are illiterate). Others outside that elite rank are renegade free-thinkers and rebellious malcontents in the eyes of the CS. Anybody who *teaches* people to read and write, those who secretly *collect* books (pretty much books of any kind and origin, but especially the works of Erin Tarn and books from pre-Rifts times), *writers* who create new books, poetry and newsletters, *printers* (which includes underground presses and factions within the Black Market who sell anything if makes it a buck, including the works of Erin Tarn and other banned material from pre-Cataclysmic comic books and novels to history books and science journals), *distributors, smugglers* and *booksellers* who traffic in books are treasonous dissidents bent on destroying the CS. They are to be flushed out of hiding and terminated whenever possible. The curious individual who reads only occasionally and even the inquisitive City Rat or street urchin who can't read a word but who "holds, hides and delivers" books for

Rogue Scholars, collectors, smugglers or the Black Market are typically threatened, beaten and their book(s) taken from them (sometimes ripped up, burned or blasted to smithereens on the spot). Those working for booksellers, printers, smugglers and scholars may be interrogated and forced to reveal who they work for and where books and/or printing facilities are hidden. Then a full scale CS raid or shakedown is made on the place, the books seized and taken away for evaluation or destroyed right there, and those responsible shot where they stand for acts of sedition to undermine and overthrow the government of the Coalition States. Book burnings and hangings of book dealers are commonplace in the 'Burbs.

Perhaps needless to say, this extreme position has made books, old films, television shows, and books or film transferred to computer/video disks (text or audio), as well as other pre-Rifts artifacts, are hot commodities in the 'Burbs. They are offered through many underground and illegal venues and there are no shortage of buyers. The CS fails to realize that it is *human nature* to a) want what is forbidden, and b) want to learn about one's history/past. Consequently, many folks, including the illiterate majority, find it appealing to own something, whether it's bottle caps and candy wrappers to books, films or relics, from the past. Furthermore, the Coalition's attack on books and literacy compels some people to want to learn how to read and learn for themselves what the CS doesn't want them to know. It also turns bookworms, teachers, scholars, historians and scientists into heroes and rebels whether they want to be or not. Heroes that many residents of the 'Burbs willingly help to escape Coalition punishment.

It should be pointed out that anyone who turns books and other contraband over to the Coalition authorities are given a special badge of honor (which is prestigious for loyalists like

those living in the Old Towns), plus some sort of minor reward such as a bag of candy, ice cream, bottle of booze, a loaf of bread and cheese, or a few credits (4D6). If a number of items (more than ten) are turned over to authorities, or if the item is rare or hated, the individual might get a reward of 50-100 credits and/or a day pass to inside the fortress city, in addition to the badge of honor and a treat. This encourages loyalists and the poor to turn in items they might find on the street rather than try to resell them to visitors or back to the Black Market or underground book and antiquities dealers.

Pre-Rifts Films & Television

Unrestricted pre-Rifts films, movies and televison shows are also taboo. The Coalition government is careful to control, edit, restrict and ban what it deems to be appropriate or inappropriate for CS society. Films and televison shows about civil rights, slavery, Nazi Germany, genocide, freedom of expression, etc., as well as the American Revolution and fun, happy movies that promote the value of freedom of speech, equality and education are all censored and banned by the CS for fear they might give their citizens "wrong" ideas. In other words, anything that might give people a reason to consider a way of life other than that promoted by the CS. For this reason, historical documents are also censored or edited to promote Coalition ideals.

Going to the movies. Since the people of the Coalition States are already conditioned to watch "film" for their news, information and entertainment, old films and television have a huge potential audience. Furthermore, thousands upon thousands of pre-Rifts films, documentaries and television programs have survived on digital disks of various types, all of which have been for entrepreneurs of Rifts Earth to display and copy onto present day technology. The Black Market and independent film duplicators and dealers can charge top dollar for most films *banned* by the CS (50-200 credits, sometimes more; averages at around 100 credits). Similarly, underground theaters, known as "historyplexes," "sin-o-plexes" and "dark-houses," can pack the seats when they show particularly exciting or rare films. Admission at the door can vary from as little as 5-10 credits if the theater is out in the sticks where people are poor and the film is dull, pedestrian or of poor visual quality (usually from bad duplication), to 20-80 credits a person for the *good stuff*: rare, controversial, exciting, scary, or of outstanding quality. Average cost is 20-40 on average and sometimes includes a double feature (two films or a film and a short like a half-hour to an hour of TV cartoons or comedy show); only 5-10 credits for films and movies approved (and possibly edited) by the CS.

The Black Market and other underground film exhibitors are fastidious and ruthless in keeping films that pack the house off the "video-disk" market and send the "good stuff" on a regular viewing circuit. Many of these underground theaters will keep the same "hot" film for weeks or months; i.e., keep showing the same one titles until the crowds start to thin. The typical "dark-house" is fairly small, seating an audience of 100-300, but can be as small as seating 20-50 or large enough for as many as a thousand or two (these are usually found at kingdoms outside the Coalition territory, not the 'Burbs). Sometimes a regular theater is used, showing films illegally after hours to a private audience (may be done with or without the theater owner's knowledge and approval).

Pre-Rifts Artifacts

Not all pre-Rifts artifacts are banned or considered dangerous. Extremely common items like pottery, china, coffee mugs, coins, jewelry, bottles, bottle caps, most toys, food and beverage cans, silverware, hand tools (screwdriver, scissors, etc.), clothes and other basic utensils and knicknacks are generally considered harmless and okay to sell and own. Such articles, particularly coins, jewelry, bottles, cans, toys, baseball caps and certain articles of clothes, get very good prices from collectors of ancient memorabilia, as well as from the wealthy and powerful, a growing number of whom are starting to think collections of antiquities are prestigious. Still, CS authorities are not too thrilled about such collectors, fearing it will go from the legal to wanting forbidden items and a desire to learn more about the "real" past.

Ancient artifacts that are banned include pre-Rifts weapons (namely high-tech energy weapons), advanced body armor, advanced technology (including medical and industrial), and anything that is military or NEMA (the pre-Rifts national defense force in North America), in addition to books and films. Additionally, many works of art are illegal (or at least coveted for the Coalition's own museums, secret archives and private collectors). Ancient weapons like swords, knives and projectile weapons/guns, as well as most tools and other basic items have been knocked off and marketed for generations, besides it is difficult to prove something is the genuine, historical article. It is high-tech, written and cultural material that the Coalition States covets for themselves and wants kept out of the mainstream.

Remember, much of Chi-Town's and the Coalition States' own advanced technology, weapons and vehicles (including SAMAS, Skelebots, Sky-Cycles, tanks, and others) are copies of, or based on, pre-Rifts technology they unearthed decades earlier and reverse engineered to make their own. These are advancements and secrets the CS wants to keep for themselves. Furthermore, the CS has claimed to have invented many of these items as part of their publicity and propaganda campaign. Since most are rare military items, nobody can effectively prove otherwise, and any books, films, or documentation literally dug up by Rogue Scholars, unauthorized historians and outsiders can be denied and disputed as convincing "fakes" created to discredit the Coalition States.

Alien Technology

Alien technology falls into the same basic category as old, pre-Rifts technology in that the CS either wants it for themselves or want it out of the hands of rivals. On the other hand, the xenophobic, human-centric CS government genuinely distrusts alien technology and tends to ignore, lock away or destroy anything that is too alien/strange, beyond their comprehension or even hints of magic. Basic alien gizmos and weapons whose purpose can be recognized are usually ignored by CS authorities in the 'Burbs, unless they want the item for themselves, at which point the item in question will be confiscated as alien contra-band (". . . and you should be glad we're taking it and letting you off with only a warning"). Alien technology that is easily overlooked (nano-items, force fields, and advanced communication systems among them) aren't even noticed 90% of the time. Obvious "weird" looking items are confiscated, but even then the owner is just given a stern warning, and beaten or killed only if he tries to make a run for it or fights back. Likewise, anything that appears to be magical (even if it isn't) may be seized as contraband, though in these cases the CS authorities are likely to want to question the owner and use lethal force at the slightest hesitation or protest.

Streets of Opportunity The Chi-Town 'Burbs

The war in Tolkeen has come to a cataclysmic end. The kingdom of magic lays in ruin, its people scattered to the wind, its leaders, educators and heroes hunted by the Coalition Army like animals to be put down. Survivors and the disenfranchised are making their way to other, safer lands, and are already starting to show up at the Chi-Town 'Burbs. Some of these people search for loved ones gone missing in action, others for work and a means (any means) to support themselves and their families. Others come to the 'Burbs to lose themselves among the masses. Still others arrive clutching valuables to sell. Some are personal items salvaged from destruction and offered by the true owners; many, however, are valuables found or looted during the war, and half the sellers don't even know they may hold in their hands ancient, magical and forbidden knowledge and artifacts.

With the war over, mercenaries and adventurers from both sides of the conflict are also limping their way out of the battlefield and back to civilization. Some return home. Some come to lick their wounds or to find a little rest and relaxation before their next assignment. Others come to cash in on booty "acquired" (one way or another) while in Tolkeen or on the way home.

Following behind these people are the *vultures of war*: scavengers, looters, smugglers, thieves, and murderers who know darn well what they have in hand and seek to sell their ill-gotten gains to the highest bidder. In this case, the booty is often books, magic and other contraband torn from the hands of the dead, dug out from under collapsed buildings, or stolen from Tolkeenites at gunpoint. These professionals go right to the Black Market, underground shops, collectors and adventurers who they think will give them a good price. Unscrupulous scum to begin with, they have no qualms about selling items to members of the Federation of Magic, enemies of the Coalition States, dragons, demons or any evil buyers. Likewise, they ignore pleas from refugees and heroes who may claim the items have been stolen from them or who represent a righteous cause, unless they have the credits to *buy* the items back.

Right behind the vultures are the predators still on the prowl, bounty hunters, assassins, CS agents and adventurers turned man-hunters searching for "war criminals" and "treasure" wanted by the CS and for which a bounty or reward is offered. They follow the trail of their quarry wherever it leads, and for many, that trail leads to the Chi-Town 'Burbs.

Among all of these motley batches of people are also fugitives, the homeless, ex-Tolkeen freedom fighters, spies (from many fronts, including the CS and Federation of Magic), practitioners of magic, dragons and other beings magically transformed to look human, as well as Tolkeenites turned terrorists in search of revenge. The 'Burbs are ideal for these so-called **Retribution Squads** on many levels. **1.** They can lose themselves in the anonymous masses of the 'Burbs where they can lay low while they plot their next act of murderous revenge. **2.** They can acquire stolen relics, artifacts and magic (especially magic items) from the vultures who stole them and use them in their cause. **3.** The 'Burbs give them easy access to Coalition forces (CS soldiers and police) who they can target for death. **4.** They can also wait and watch, like man-hunters, to find and kill the CS hired bounty hunters, spies and soldiers who fought against them in the war. This range of targets also includes known independent adventurers, heroes, and individuals who opposed the war or refused to join the battle to save Tolkeen. Remember, many of these self-proclaimed "patriots" are as fanatical and evil as their reviled enemy, and they see many noble and honorable individuals as traitors, turncoats, and enemies because they didn't share their view or choose to fight for their cause. The worst are absolute cold-blooded killers and madmen bent on exacting revenge on all their enemies, including Erin Tarn, Cyber-Knights and Lazlo. **Note:** More on Retribution Squads in the **Final Siege** and **Aftermath of War** World Books and the next **Rifts® Adventure Sourcebook: The Tolkeen Crisis.**

The bottom line is, the Chi-Town 'Burbs is one of the most sought after destination points, because it offers the greatest opportunity for people from all walks of life, D-Bees included and humans in particular. Here survivors, looters, wizards and warriors can all find a place to stay and some kind of work. Those with booty to sell can find a buyer to purchase whatever they may have, provided it has genuine value. Fugitives find the 'Burbs an attractive place to lay low, for a little while anyway. First, they can hide in plain sight among the mass of humanity that fills the streets. Second, there are a vast number of "outlets" for buying and selling goods – both over the counter and illegal. Third, the 'Burbs provide a vast range of contacts, opportunities and resources a fugitive may need to survive and move on. In short, the Chi-Town 'Burbs have a little bit of ev-

erything anybody might need. D-Bees and practitioners of magic have to be more subtle and careful, but they too can find what they need in the 'Burbs, whether it be a roof over their head, fake identification documents, bionic upgrades, a smuggler to buy their contraband loot or an avenue of escape.

And when opportunity knocks, the people of the 'Burbs embrace it with open arms, and that's exactly what the fall of Tolkeen means to the 'Burbs: opportunity (at least in the short term). Likewise, other scavengers and scoundrels are arriving to take advantage of the situation, namely agents from the Federation of Magic, Atlantis and other kingdoms that oppose the CS, hoping to purchase magical artifacts, weapons and secrets. Many minor, major and super-rare magic artifacts were gathered by the Tolkeen forces, and now that the kingdom has fallen, many of those items will hit the streets, with the Chi-Town 'Burbs being a primary marketplace.

Even in the shadow of Chi-Town, the 'Burbs have always offered a large range of legal and illegal goods, services and activity, at least for those who know where to find them. For those who don't, there are City Rats, Cyber-Snatchers, Black Marketeers, thieves and others skilled at recognizing people in need to direct them where to go, for a price. Others are good at recognizing fresh meat to victimize, chew up and spit out, or lead astray. Adventurers and mercenaries can usually find work as "guns-for-hire," bodyguards and bounty hunters if they want it. As for selling goods, half the time those who prowl the streets and deal in contraband can find the seller if it's worth their trouble (i.e. is profitable enough), plus there are dozens of pawnshops, fences, private entrepreneurs (crooks, thieves and smugglers only too glad to help line their own pockets) and Black Market outlets to buy, sell or trade a large range of illegal goods and services. One can buy or sell almost anything common to North America to somebody in the Chi-Town 'Burbs, from "used" bionic parts, vehicles and weapons to magic items, illegal drugs and banned books.

Of course the CS does not allow anything too *alien,* dangerous or outrageous on its doorstep, so contraband items and services must be handled discreetly and underground. Furthermore, if the Coalition authorities catch wind of a particularly powerful or deadly magic relic or alien weapon, they'll search for it themselves and may launch a shakedown and/or a purge if they strongly suspect it is located in a specific area. That means dealers, traders, buyers and teachers of magic, literacy, history and the alien must conduct their business in the shadows without fanfare and constantly be on the lookout for Coalition forces intent on shutting them down, probably killing *everybody* involved in the transaction. Still, secret schools, book dealers, purveyors of magic, and other things banned by the CS are found scattered throughout the 'Burbs, particularly in the New Town and Shanty Town 'Burbs.

A flood of the forbidden. What worries the CS is that with Tolkeen's collapse, vast treasure troves of magic, books and forbidden knowledge have vanished, looted by rebels, freedom fighters, thieves, and refugees, or carried away by those intent on preserving the knowledge and those who need to sell it for their own survival. Coalition authorities know that a good amount of that material will find its way to the Chi-Town 'Burbs (estimates suggest as much as 40-50%) where it may fall into the wrong hands, i.e., not the Coalition's and into those of its enemies. This has instigated an increased campaign of patrols, law enforcement and surveillance in the 'Burbs, particularly the *New Towns* where it is mostly likely to change hands and *Shanty Towns* where it first comes in. Coalition forces are also looking closely for practitioners of magic who may be refugees, war criminals and buyers from the Federation of Magic or Atlantis.

Firetown
A New Town 'Burb

1. Hayley, Mind Melter for Hire

Hayley Chonlan is a 19-year old Mind Melter on a mission: to find her sister. The Chonlan family arrived at the Chi-Town 'Burbs when Hayley was 11. Unfortunately, Hayley's parents were ill-equipped for the harsh and dangerous 'Burb life. Within a matter of a few months, both of them were dead, leaving Hayley and her sister, Jenni (who was older by 4 years), alone in the world.

For the next several years, Jenni acted as the surrogate parent for her younger sibling. When Hayley's psychic powers first manifested a few years later, it was Jenni who helped her kid sister keep her sanity through the traumatic time of becoming psychic and getting the subsequent Identification Coding (IC)

process. The two sisters became very close, sometimes adopting a "You and me against the world" attitude.

Things finally started looking good for the sisters a couple of years ago. Jenni had fallen in love with Gar Semple, a young CS Grunt. The pair were engaged to be married and Jenni would be moved up the CS Citizenship list (with Hayley likely to follow). Then disaster struck.

Gar was lost on a patrol mission and presumed dead. A few months afterward, Jenni vanished without a trace. Hayley has been searching for Jenni ever since, but without a single clue or lead . . . it has been a painful and sad process. Those who know Hayley believe it is an exercise in futility, but the young woman insists she would know (psychically) if her sister was dead, and she's not. Unfortunately, those same psychic powers have been unable to locate Jenni, so the search continues. Hayley has scoured the 'Burb of Firetown and several of the neighboring 'Burbs and favorite haunts of her sister, but has come up empty. As of late, she has started to hire herself out to adventurers and mercenaries as a local guide and a psychic for hire, using her psychic talents to do odd jobs and assist in missions away from the 'Burbs. She hopes by associating with outsiders, particularly adventurers, she might get a lead on her sister's whereabouts. While "out on a job," Hayley asks her employers if they may have seen or heard anything about her sister, Jenni, or an MIA Coalition soldier known as Corporal Gar Semple. She also discreetly asks (and reads the minds of) those she meets along the way.

Hayley is working on a number of assumptions. 1. She knew Jenni was pining away for her fiancé missing in action; she could feel her pain. 2. Though Jenni never actually spoke of it, Hayley's psionic powers picked up a number of stray thoughts about her sister going out into the wilderness to see if she could find Gar. 3.Though she had no psionic abilities, Jenni insisted she knew Gar was alive and needed her. 4. Hayley found out that Jenni had picked up some wilderness supplies and gear she had ordered the night she vanished. Conclusion: Hayley is currently working on the belief that her grief-stricken sister ran off that night to search for Gar somewhere out in the wilderness. Knowing Jenni, she wouldn't have endangered her kid sister on such a harebrained venture, though it seems equally unlikely that Jenni would have just run off without leaving at least a note. Hayley realizes she could be wrong and that her sister might have been abducted and sold into slavery, which is why she also keeps an eye out for slavers, and tries to keep an open mind for any possible leads in directions she has not considered.

Hiring herself out to anyone who needs her psychic abilities helps to finance her private search for her sister and takes her in directions and places she might not have otherwise considered (hoping that the hand of fate might put her on the right path).

Hayley has proven to be a reliable, cagey and resourceful hired hand, using her psychic abilities to avoid danger, find people and get the group out of trouble. She has even found that she enjoys adventuring, as much as she can while consumed by her private mission. Any information that might help her find her sister given in good faith is not forgotten and Hayley will feel she owes that individual a favor in the future. On the other hand, those who pretend to know something to either mess with her or to lead her on for their own purpose, as well as those who deliberately attempt to avoid paying her the credits they owe her, bring out the worst in the Mind Melter, and her powers usually tell her when someone is trying to deceive or cheat her.

Hayley was originally adamant that Jenni is still alive somewhere, but with each false trail and dead end, she grows more discouraged and desperate. If her search efforts continue without success, she could be a powder keg just waiting to ignite.

Adventure Hooks: Player characters encountering Hayley may find her out in the wilderness with another group who has hired her, or following up a lead on her own, or hanging around Firetown looking for work. She talks to any adventurers she runs into and tells them about her quest to find her sister. Anyone who can provide her with information or possible leads about Jenni will make a loyal friend and ally. Anyone who offers to assist her in her search can be taken on any number of adventures to almost anywhere. Hayley usually has 1-4 possible leads. (A slaver group that was visiting Firetown when Jenni went missing and they are back in the region at [fill in the blank]. Or a mercenary team she worked for once saw a woman matching Jenni's description, and though they spoke to her and

she claimed to be someone else, Hayley feels compelled to check it out. Or Hayley had a dream about [someplace, some person, some monster] and wonders, could it have been a premonition? She needs to go and find out. Or Hayley has recently found out where Gar went missing. Presumably Jenni went that way. Maybe the same person has them both? Of course the G.M. can work up any of his or her own. Hayley could be a useful vehicle to get the player group to go on a particular adventure or place.)

Here are some possible adventure ideas involving Hayley's quest. Exactly how or why the adventure group gets hooked up with her is left to the G.M. Remember, Hayley tries to follow every lead she comes across, so she can take the player characters almost anywhere.

1. Trapped in the 'Burbs. An outfit of evil miscreants (humans or D-Bees) operating out of one of the other 'Burbs has been snatching women and forcing them into slave labor. These villains could be a group that has gotten cocky with power, such as a street gang, Cyber-Snatchers, Slavers, criminal outfit, a group led by a Shifter, sex-slave ring, etc. The only way to find out if they have Jenni is to infiltrate the group, pose as fellow underworld crooks or as potential buyers (of whatever it is they have to offer) or to raid the place and see what shakes loose. The last option has its problems, one, the criminals and workers will scatter and if Jenni is there, the group might miss her, and two, if enough noise and trouble is made, a Coalition patrol is likely to appear on the scene.

2. The CS connection. During an adventure in the 'Burbs or the wilderness, the group encounters a Coalition Officer turned rogue. He hears Hayley or some member of the group asking about Gar and/or Jenni, and decides to pipe up. "I know them. Dead? Lost?" he chuckles, "quite the contrary." According to this guy, Gar had minor psionics and volunteered for an experimental mind boost and the opportunity to work in Psi-Battalion. Turned out his girlfriend did too, only she was a Burbie and had to "disappear" without a trace to be recruited by Psi-Battalion. This rogue Coalition Officer insists the story is true and that Jenni and Gar are super-elite Psi-Battalion agents – assuming the psionic boosting process didn't kill them. Psychic probes indicate that he certainly believes what he is saying is true. But is it? Jenni never exhibited psionic abilities. Then again, Hayley never could read her thoughts when Jenni didn't want her to. Could that have been Mind Block or Mind Block Auto-Defense in action? Could this be true? How do they find out?

3. Follow a trail to Gar. Hayley has plucked Gar's last CS assignment out of the head of an old CS comrade or his commanding officer during a chance (friendly) meeting in the 'Burbs. This is the best lead she has had in months. If Jenni went after Gar, this is likely the path she followed. Actually, Game Masters could weave together a string of adventures, one after the other, as Hayley and the player group follow every possible lead along the trail. The player group may be with her because of the promise of treasure/reward or revenge along the way or because they like her or because she has hired *them*.

A string of adventures could include any or all of the following, and then some.

a) The group comes across a village that has recently been raided by Xiticix or Simvan Monster Riders. Several villagers have been carried off by the raiders, including a young, human woman fitting Jenni's description. The woman was found wandering the woods with no memory not long after Jenni disappeared (or it could be a male fitting Gar's description. It might be fun and nice to find the missing soldier first, leading up to reuniting everybody). The group has to find and then rescue the person (and all of the villagers?) in question. This could be yet another false lead or the real thing. If they find Gar, the need to find Jenni seems all the more imperative.

b) Local people know about a CS soldier who has gone rogue and has established himself in a little village kingdom of his own. They cheerfully point the group in the right direction. When the group arrives, they find the fellow chumming around with a squad of Coalition soldiers. He is not Gar but it seems he has a deal going on with corrupt soldiers and mercenaries, but mostly Coalition soldiers, who come to him to fence Tolkeen artifacts, magic items and other contraband, including CS weapons. He takes a 33% cut for his troubles (actually he skims an extra 10% off of non-Coalition personnel) as the middleman and everybody is happy. This soldier, calling himself Jason King, has Black Market connections with both the *Chi-Town 'Burbs* in the east and *Bandito Arms* in the west. He is also developing some connections in the Pecos Empire who are willing to pay top dollar for Coalition and other high-powered weapons, armor and vehicles. He is really Lieutenant Andrew Kingsley, missing in action since the slaughter of the Sorcerers' Revenge near Tolkeen. His body was recently recovered and he has been officially counted among the dead, so he is no longer MIA – he's officially dead and able to develop his new life as Jason King. The fake body was set up by his corrupt buddies who claim to have rescued Lieutenant Kingsley from a band of Tolkeen Terrorists. As the story goes, the lieutenant got "misted" – vaporized in the ensuing pursuit by the villains. All the soldiers could recover was his pinky finger which has been DNA confirmed to be Lt. Andrew Kingsley. Case closed.

Jason King and his CS associates are leery of outsiders and his old Army chums will suddenly pretend to be on a routine patrol checking the village for any trouble. They will shoot the player group a glance, and ask them if they mean any trouble. If Hayley tells them about her quest (and why not), one of the grunts may actually know about Gar, and relate when and how he went missing but other than some details, has no new leads to offer. There are no problems if the group moves on or accepts Jason's cover story. In fact, he could become a means through which they can trade or sell weapons and loot. However, if they threaten his budding little enterprise the group will find themselves wanted by the Coalition as spies, Tolkeen resistance fighters or worse. King and his army buddies have enough connections and pull to make life miserable for any they choose, and not just with the CS, he could get Pecos Bandits on their tails too. The villagers are happy with their new leader and feel safer now that Coalition soldiers regularly visit.

c) Slaver. He and his band of minions find Hayley's plight amusing and refuse to tell her anything they know without a thousand Universal Credits or some kind of fair trade. This dirt bag doesn't know anything of use to Hayley or the group. However, while they are present, the adventurers see plenty of innocent people, mostly Psi-Stalker and human women and children, caged like animals. Some plead for help, others just stare or hide their faces. Is the group in a position to help? Do they?

d) An encounter with bandits. They know nothing and could care less, but they don't intend to walk away empty handed. Unless the group is willing to give up half their gear and vehicles, a fight will ensue. Fortunately, the bandits are not as tough as they seem to think they are and the player group can fight them off with relative ease, though they earn the bandits' lasting enmity.

e) An old Tolkeen Monster Squad (doesn't have to be near Tolkeen, they may be on the run). The G.M. can determine the exact mix though a Brodkil or two and a Witchling or Black Faerie are probably among them (can be smaller than a typical squad). These villains are bold and nasty. One of them is finishing eating a large animal and the pile of bones nearby look frighteningly human (a character with medical or biology skills will know they are). If asked about Jenni or Gar the creatures start to giggle and taunt the group about humans, the Tolkeen war and why should they help them. Finally, one grins and announces, "I remember that woman. Yes, sometime back. I remember her well, she was my plaything for a month and tasted wonderful when I chose to eat her." His buddies laugh and agree. If Hayley keeps her wits she can determine psionically that the monster is lying and knows nothing. However, these creatures' behavior is far from endearing and they may make a few threatening gestures and comments that could set Hayley or one of the other adventurers off. Killing these fiends can only make the world a better place, and the G.M. *may* exacerbate the situation by having a humanoid prisoner or two in the monsters' clutches; of course the prisoners are a future meal waiting to happen.

f) The adventurer group encounters a band of nomads or fellow adventurers who mistake them for Coalition spies or bounty hunters working for the CS. Hayley can tell they know about a woman who fits Jenni's general description (they don't know her name) and that they recently escorted her someplace safe, but that's all she can get from telepathic skims of their surface thoughts and they refuse to admit even that. These people are convinced the group are CS agents, how can they be convinced otherwise? If their minds can be changed, or if they can be tricked or forced into revealing the location, that will be the next lead to follow. Only it takes the group to a band of Tolkeen survivors on the run. Most are practitioners of magic, and a cell of evil sorcerers of which this woman is a member, and no, she isn't Hayley's sister. Problem is, now that the player group has managed to find them, the sorcerers can't allow them to live. To escape the group must fight.

g) Coalition forces. Gar went MIA in this region because the CS is locked in a conflict with . . . whatever the G.M. wants: Bandits, Simvan, Xiticix, Tolkeen rebels, the Federation of Magic, a new (secret?) threat, or something else. That means there is some danger/evil plus CS troops everywhere. Which side does the player group fall on, or do they get caught in the middle? Does anybody, CS soldier or otherwise, know anything about Gar? Do they think he's dead? Have they seen Jenni?

h) The horror. According to a villager, woodsman, traveling mage or someone, he distinctly remembers an attractive young woman named Jenni looking for someone, a husband or fiancé. Sweet girl, he recalls. He couldn't help her find her man, but later learned that she was taken captive by some evil being going around turning humans into giant (10 foot/3 m tall) monsters. Doesn't know much about the actual villain, only that it has a hate for humans and delights in turning them into monsters. According to rumor, this being is building an army to send against Coalition forces in the area. Doesn't know much else other than the story is true. He saw the poor Jenni-Creature after the transformation. She had managed to escape and came to him for help, only there was no magic he knew that could transform her back to normal. He knows of someone who probably can (and will share that info with the group), but before he could take her there, four of the monsters showed up and took her away. He tried to stop them but got knocked unconscious. It was a miracle they didn't find him and kill or transform him. The character is glad to point them in the right direction where the monsters are gathering.

To rescue the Jenni-Creature, the group will have to face the monsters and their creator: Shaartar, a Devilman Shifter driven mad by some terrible experience with the CS (may be a Tolkeen based event or entirely unrelated). He has uncovered a magical alien device that, when used at a ley line, can transform a normal human into a powerful monster. (**Note:** All monsters have supernatural P.S., energy blasts do half damage, 5D6x10 M.D.C., recover lost M.D.C. at a rate of 1D6x10 per hour and double on a ley line, have a speed of 2D6x10, P.B. 1D4, but a low animal-like I.Q. and can only growl a word or two. Most forget any skills they once knew and only have a vague recollection of their past lives. The Jenni-Creature is an exception so she suffers emotionally more than most.) The alien device can be used to reverse the process and so can a hermit who was once a powerful practitioner of magic. The reclusive mage is only one day's journey away. The Shifter has only begun his diabolical plot for revenge – his madness prevents him from being well organized or acting decisively. He cannot be reasoned with or paid off, however, nor is he willing to give up any of "his" creations. To get the Jenni-Creature and/or the alien magic device, they will have steal it and her, or face Shaartar and his monstrous minions. Other than Jenni, his other creations are loyal and obedient (she is not because Jenni, it turns out, is a minor psychic with the powers of Mind Block and Total Recall, and the latter will allow her operate the alien device because she's seen it used.) As a Shifter, Shaartar may have other demonic or monstrous minions (adjust their numbers and types to fit the player group's power level). G.M. Note: This *could be* Jenni if you'd like (especially if Gar was found earlier), or it could be a different Jenny – Jennifer Gowel, an attractive young woman searching for her husband. Whatever the case, there are a couple ways to return any and all of the monsters back into humans. Once Shaartar is slain or the device taken from him, his control over them is broken. If the group has the device, the monsters will follow and obey them. If not, the beasts will have to be bound and forced to come along. Thankfully, their experiences as monsters are mostly forgotten when returned to normal, and seems like a bad dream even to Jennifer.

4. One possible happy ending (if everything goes well). Jenni Chonlan is alive and well in New Lazlo. Gar Semple was wounded and lost consciousness during the Sorcerers' Revenge near Tolkeen (or one of the campaigns in that war). He awoke to find that he had been found and given medical treatment by a group of refugees; D-Bees no less. Turns out his benefactors were actually innocent victims of Coalition atrocities, but despite their suffering, could not let a fellow living being perish when they had the power to save him. It was then that Gar real-

ized the CS High Command had gone too far and lied about D-Bees being evil monsters. Gar deserted the CS and joined the refugees on their trek to New Lazlo.

Gar wanted to retrieve both of the Chonlan sisters and bring them to New Lazlo where they could live a better life, but was still too badly wounded to do this. Instead, the Council of New Lazlo sent a team of adventurers who volunteered to infiltrate the Chi-Town 'Burbs and return with the girls. Unfortunately, the adventurers couldn't find Hayley who was off secretly practicing her developing psionic powers. Scant seconds after finding Jenni, they were attacked by a CS patrol and had to make a run for it, spiriting away Jenni in the process. The CS patrol had mistaken them for saboteurs from the Federation of Magic, and gave chase halfway to Michigan before they gave up. Leaving like that was the hardest and most heartbreaking decision that Jenni Chonlan ever had to make. She did provide for a message to be sent to her sister; unfortunately, the messenger was killed in a street brawl before he could find Hayley.

Since that time, Gar and Jenni (who are now citizens of New Lazlo) have prevailed upon the New Lazlo Council to send another team of adventurers to find and bring Hayley to New Lazlo or at least send another message, but other, more pressing matters consume their attention. Gar has considered going back himself, but it is too dangerous for him, and he won't let Jenni go, especially in her condition – she'll give birth to their first child in two months.

The Player Characters could be a group of adventurers on their way (or may already be in the 'Burbs) to find and retrieve Hayley and bring her "home" to Jenni and Gar in New Lazlo (Ann Arbor, Michigan). They are under orders to keep a low profile and not attract unwanted attention. Thus, they should take their time in their search for Hayley Chonlan.

A few adventure twists and turns: 1. Turns out Hayley is the one in trouble. The survivors from the latest group to have hired the young Mind Melter report she was taken captive by . . . Could be almost anything or anyone: A cell of Tolkeen Retributionists or monsters who attacked the group because they stumbled onto one of their plans. A lot of innocent people would get hurt so Hayley and company tried to stop them. They failed and now they have her. Or the villains could be from the Federation of Magic, Splugorth Slavers, bandits, Xiticix, an evil dragon, Coalition troops, or whatever. The player characters now have to rescue her before they can bring her back.

2. Hayley is out following her latest (false) lead in her search for her sister. She's been gone for some time now. Could she be in trouble? How long does the group wait? Do they get into trouble while waiting?

3. Gar can't stand it anymore. Nothing would make his wife happier than to have her kid sister at her side when the baby is born, so he has run off to find Hayley. On the way there (or back) he runs into the player group and begs for their assistance. He can pay them, but not much. Adventure follows, and at some point, Coalition soldiers get involved. If Gar is recognized, he will be arrested and taken into custody for interrogation and *execution* as a deserter and traitor. Now what? Hayley will want to mount a rescue! She can pay more, though nowhere near enough to risk one's life. Do the player characters help out of the goodness of their hearts (or revenge on the CS)? If so they need to act now, before Gar is taken inside the fortress city. Of course

even a successful rescue of Gar will brand the player group, Gar and Hayley as members of a Tolkeen Retribution Squad. And the group had better make sure they aren't followed back to New Lazlo, because if they are, that peaceful community will be mistakenly added to the Coalition's list of hostile magic communities to be eradicated!

Note: On the other hand, Hayley could go on adventure after adventure without ever finding her sister, providing all kinds of adventure possibilities for her friends/bosses/teammates (i.e., the player characters, hint, hint). As a low level character, she could even be adopted and used as a player character if somebody would like.

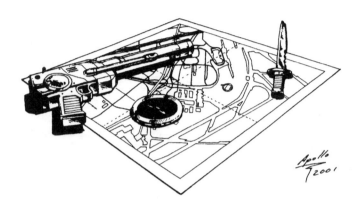

Hayley Chonlan Quick Stats

Real Name: Hayley Chonlan.

Aliases: None.

Alignment: Unprincipled.

Attributes: I.Q. 13, M.E. 15, M.A. 11, P.S. 10, P.P. 13, P.E. 20, P.B. 15, Spd. 12

Hit Points: 32 and **S.D.C.:** 14.

Weight: 117 pounds (53 kg). **Height:** 5 feet, 8 inches (1.75 m). **Age:** 19.

P.P.E.: 10. **I.S.P.:** 162.

Disposition: First and foremost, Hayley is a survivor. She is still a decent person but is becoming more hardened and driven as worry about her sister is taking its toll on her. She is clever, resourceful and fiercely independent.

Experience Level: 4th level Mind Melter (closing in on 5th level).

Magic Knowledge: None.

Psychic Powers: Super-Psionics: Bio-Manipulation (10), Bio-Regeneration (super; 20), Electrokinesis (varies), Group Mind Block (22), Mentally Possess Others (30), Mind Bolt (varies), and Telekinetic Force Field (30).

Other Psionics: Alter Aura (2), Death Trance (1), Detect Psionics (6), Empathy (4), Impervious to Fire (4), Mind Block (4), Induce Sleep (4), Levitation (varies), Object Read (6), Presence Sense (4), Psychic Diagnosis (4), Psychic Purification (8), Resist Fatigue (4), Resist Thirst (6), See Aura (6), See the Invisible (4), Sixth Sense (2), Summon Inner Strength (4), and Telepathy (4). Considered a Master Psionic/Mind Melter with 162 I.S.P.; requires a 10 or higher to save vs psionic attack. **Attacks per Melee:** Five physical or psionic attacks.

Bonuses: +2 to parry, +2 to dodge, +2 to roll with impact, +2 to pull punch, kick attack does 1D6 S.D.C., +3 to save vs poison and magic, +10% to save vs coma/death.

Skills of Note: Speaks American, Spanish, and Techno-Can, all at 90%, Basic Mechanics 55%, Computer Hacking 30%, Concealment 42%, Detect Ambush 55%, Detect Concealment 50%, Lore: Psychic 50%, Pick Locks 45%, Pilot Automobile 67%, Pilot Motorcycle 73%, Prowl 50%, Streetwise 42% and Hand to Hand: Basic.

Weapon Proficiencies: W.P. Revolver and W.P. Energy Pistol, both at 4th level proficiency.

Weapons & Armor: Hayley has a .38 revolver and a Wilk's 320 laser pistol for whenever her psionic powers are depleted. Wears a modified suit of Plastic Man body armor (35 M.D.C.) made to look less bulky and more shapely. She cannot afford better armor since she puts as much money as possible toward her quest to find her sister.

Money: Most everything she earns goes into basic living expenses and her quest to find her sister.

Description: Hayley is an attractive young, human woman with long brown hair and sparkling blue eyes.

2. Karl's Revenge

An out of the way bar that serves hard liquor and attracts human supremacists and the staunchest supporters of Emperor Prosek and the Coalition States. That having been said, the patrons love to muck it up with "D-Bee lovers," "sorcerous scum," "anti-Coalition losers," and "bleeding heart Tarnits." Tarnit is the slang label for people who espouse the views of Erin Tarn. In fact, the regulars at Karl's Revenge so dislike the rabble-rousing historian, Erin Tarn, that there are two dart boards with Erin Tarn's face taped to them (riddled with holes), and what is supposed to be a life-sized likeness of the woman painted on a punching bag in the *Philosopher's Corner* where customers can punctuate their anti-Tarn statements with blows to the bag. The Philosopher's Corner is also where Tarnits, panhandlers, critics of the Coalition States or Emperor Prosek, and outspoken advocates of free speech and rights for D-Bees are taken to have the snot beaten out of them.

This sentiment makes the bar a happy watering hole for Coalition military personnel on leave, as well as soldiers and police on duty who slip in to grab a quick drink or a bit to eat before going back on patrol (CS soldiers and police get a 50% discount on everything in the bar). Bounty hunters, mercenaries, scouts, adventurers and Psi-Stalkers who work for the Coalition Army also find this establishment a good place to unwind and share tales of hunting down, capturing, tormenting and killing "enemies of the States" with little fear of retribution or being ostracized for their harsh, pro-CS views and cruel antics in the field. Here people regularly talk cheerfully about CS policies, the Prosek family, war, killing D-Bees, wiping out the Federation of Magic and similar topics. This kind of patriotic talk, washed down with several rounds of liquor, also makes Karl's Revenge a place of *inspiration* for mob justice ("let's go lynch us some *@#$%# D-Bees") and random acts of mindless violence, intimidation, terrorism, and vandalism in the name of the Emperor and the Coalition States – usually for the purpose of showing "them" who is boss (whoever "them" might be for that night).

Of course, their targets are usually nonhumans, practitioners of magic and those who openly speak against the Great and Noble Emperor Karl Prosek or the Coalition States.

With the fall of Tolkeen stirring up all kinds of negative talk about the Coalition Army, the government and Emperor, as well as bringing in refugees, freedom fighters, sorcerers and others who fought on the side of Tolkeen or supported the enemy's cause, these bullies have plenty of new targets to victimize.

Adventure Hooks: The obvious brawl and troublemaker scenarios are clear, but there are other avenues for adventure. If one is looking to find and meet with a particular CS soldier or ISS officer assigned to patrols in or around the Firetown 'Burb, then Karl's Revenge is a likely place to find him, or someone he knows. The reasons for meeting with a Coalition cop or soldier can be many. Some reasons include: **1.** To secretly (or at least quietly) pass information to CS authorities. **2.** To get information and rumors from CS authorities. Get a guy drunk enough and he might reveal everything he knows. Corrupt authorities may sell information to Burbies and what better place than at Karl's where nobody would suspect such duplicity. Or get info just by staying quiet and keeping one's ears open. **3.** To target a specific officer or soldier for a beating, kidnaping or killing. The actual dirty deed is usually done outside of Karl's, but the bar is a great place to find and follow one's quarry. **4.** To issue a warning or threat. **5.** A nice doorstep to dump a beaten and tied up criminal or Coalition soldier or lawman (the latter to issue a statement or shame the CS authorities; sometimes to make sure the poor fellow isn't killed if he were left on the street or in an alley). **6.** To make a trade or swap (CS loyalists feel safe here). **7.** To secretly (or quietly) turn over a dangerous magic item or contraband. **8.** To make contact with a "good" 'Burb patrolman; someone who can be trusted.

Other catalysts for trouble and adventure:

a) One of the workers at the bar is a snitch for the Black Market or trades information to City Rats.

b) One of the workers at the bar is really a member of the Federation of Magic and uses his position to spy on CS goings on in the 'Burbs and to target important CS operatives.

c) One of the regular patrons is a fanatical human supremacist who has a gang of skin-headed, tattooed punks who go around beating up and robbing D-Bees, Tarnits and (when possible) practitioners of magic. He hangs around the bar because he's a Coalition ISS wannabe and loves being around all these heroic figures. In addition, he figures getting to know some of these guys might help on the street if he ever gets into trouble.

d) A known watering hole for Coalition troops and bigots, the bar is regularly targeted for graffiti, rock throwing, drive-by shootings and other acts of violence (including back alley duels, and street fights). That's why the building and its windows are made of Mega-Damage materials and there are outdoor lights and surveillance systems. If the perpetrators are caught they can expect a vicious beating. If someone from the bar is killed, those responsible can expect the same street justice when they are apprehended by CS authorities or a lynch mob from the bar.

Breaux

3. Camp Fireplace

Also known as "The Camp"

A charitable organization for orphans, of which there are plenty in the 'Burbs. Life is hard and often short in the 'Burbs and even worse in the wilderness areas beyond. The lawlessness and number of rogues, criminals, mercenaries, gangs and monsters that live in or visit the 'Burbs accounts for plenty of deaths and disappearances every week. Drunken craziness, duels, brawls and clashes in the streets with the likes of Cyber-Snatchers, Slavers (Splugorth and humans), gang-bangers, inhuman predators and Coalition callousness only add to the mortality rate. Thus, a child's parent may be cut down in his or her prime of life, kidnaped and sold into slavery, killed or locked away by Coalition forces, or simply vanish, leaving their offspring alone in the world. Without someone to care for them, these children run wild in the streets and are easy victims for exploitation and foul play.

Places like Camp Fireplace function as a combination orphanage and halfway house where children are kept under adult supervision (as much as possible), looked after, given a place to sleep, provided with three square meals a day, taught some basic trade and given guidance (and maybe a little illegal schooling in reading, writing and arithmetic).

Adventure Hooks: 1. Kids will be kids and the streets of the 'Burbs call with excitement. That means from time to time a child or group of kids (1D4+2) sneak off and get into trouble. Most Coalition authorities could care less and make no effort to help runaway orphans. That leaves good Samaritans like the player characters to help.

2. One (or several) of the children have gone missing. The volunteers who run Camp Fireplace are extremely worried because nearly a dozen children have gone missing over the last few weeks and four have been found dead, gutted like fish. Word on the street is that a death cult, Witch or evil practitioner of magic is using children as human sacrifices for an as of yet unknown, but undoubtedly evil, purpose. Help anyone?

3. One of the player characters is adopted by a cute little kid who offers to be his guide to the city for an ice cream sundae or a bag of candy. If the character takes the child up on the offer or sends the kid scooting away, he (or she) will soon discover he is missing one or more valuables (ideally a credit card, but other items such as a knife, gun, radio, booze, food items, etc. are suitable substitutes). In the alternative, one or more of the characters may get entangled with a group of street urchins having fun in the streets, but soon learns or sees them snatching some things off his belt or out of his travel bag. If the character or group gives pursuit, they lose the little thieves somewhere around the Camp Fireplace Orphanage. Going to the orphanage will bring an encounter with one or more of the truly good people who run it. They dismiss any allegations that any of "their" kids could be thieves and point out that the streets are filled with ragamuffins, but they will look into the matter. "Oh, but while here, would you be so kind as to make a donation?" Followed by a long, heartfelt pitch about orphans and their needs. Staking the place out for more than eight hours will find the little thief (or band of thieves) sneaking out from the back of the building someplace and scurrying into the street. If they are observed, those watching will see them first trade stolen items for food, clothing or medicine, and then return to the orphanage where they claim "a nice adventurer bought these things." Yep, these are child-thieves with a heart of gold. It's wrong, but their hearts are in the right place. If the children are caught and dragged back to the orphanage before it's discovered what they are up to, the manager of the orphanage will exclaim there must be some mistake, these are good kids and the facility's best charity fund raisers. The kids will be punished for sneaking out, but thieves ... preposterous. Calling in the Coalition authorities will get the orphanage raided and tossed, causing a lot of damage and no results. Calling in the local authorities gets a polite inquiry and no results. **Note:** The child-thieves range in age from 9-13, levels 2-5 (Professional Thieves or Maze Rats), Unprincipled and Anarchist alignments, and know the streets and alleys of Firetown like the back of their hands. They can point the characters to all kinds of people and places – for a price.

4. City Rats under cover. Yep, a gaggle of the older kids are *Hack Rats* (see **Rifts® Bionics Sourcebook** for complete stats on all types of City Rat O.C.C.s) who deal in gathering, trading and selling information. They are mostly in it for the adventure but can be a valuable source of information in Firetown and the neighboring 'Burbs for a nice donation to the orphanage and a little bit extra in their own pockets (nothing exorbitant, but fair). They are assisted by other orphans, about 30 of which are Maze Rats, a dozen or so Pack Rats, a dozen or so are City Rat Archetypes, and another dozen or so Hero City Rats (well, as heroic as kids ages 7-18 can be). Adventures can arise if one of these City Rat orphans (or a group of them) get into trouble during one of

their escapades, especially if they were hired by the player characters to get them some information. If so, the player characters should feel obligated to get them out of trouble without involving the authorities or getting the little buggers in trouble at the orphanage (or killed). In the alternative, any characters who develop a relationship (friendship or business) with any of these kids can expect to be called upon when they or one of their pals gets into trouble. Which in turn can lead to getting the player character into trouble. **Note:** The City Rat orphans range in age from 7-18, levels 2-8, Unprincipled and Anarchist alignments, and know the streets and alleys of Firetown like the back of their hands. They also know a lot of other City Rats, gangs, other notable people and a good number of underground and criminal places of business, as well as being tapped into roughly 80% of the most current rumors and news traveling on the street grapevine in Firetown.

Note: Approximately 110 to 130 orphans are housed at the Fireplace Orphanage at any given time. Actually, the number keeps growing by 1D10 every couple of months because safe placement with good families is difficult and the orphan population keeps growing. That can only get worse with the fall of Tolkeen. Camp Fireplace can barely afford to feed and clothe the children they have, so they often recommend the *Banner Orphanage* (#19), church groups and other places. The Camp is located in the "low rent" section of town surrounded by residences. The street kids have an ongoing rivalry with those from the Banner Orphanage.

4. Fire House No. Four

This 'Burb has become notorious for its many fires, hence the relatively new name of "Firetown." Over the last 13 years half of the town has burnt down on three different occasions and there were also six other significant fires and numerous minor incidents. The worst big blaze was eight years ago, so many people believe the town is overdue for a devastating fire. 'Burb leaders insist those days are over and to make sure of it, the Firetown government has put in place the best fire and rescue department in all the Chi-Town 'Burbs. State of the art conventional fire trucks, equipment and firefighting techniques are used by the 12 well funded and staffed fire stations scattered throughout the 'Burb. The firefighters are all well-trained, half have years of experience, and Firetown has been declared to be ready for any crisis.

To further insure the 'Burb's safety, there is also an underground firefighting network in place. One the Coalition authorities would dismantle if they knew about it, but one the local leadership believes is an absolute necessity. This is a network of local volunteers to assist firefighters using *magic*. Consequently, the Firetown Volunteer M Brigade ("M" for magic) is trained to use both conventional equipment and magic items. Techno-Wizard water guns made to look like real hoses and pumps, but which magically generate the water, rain flares, and other TW gear are standard for M Brigade. Furthermore, 25% of the volunteers are Water Warlocks, 25% are Fire Warlocks, and 25% are other practitioners of magic (and creatures of magic) who know spells that can contain, extinguish and manipulate fire or water. The remaining 25% are regular volunteers with no special spell casting abilities, but who use the Techno-Wizard firefighting gadgets. Racial mix of the Firetown Fire Department is 85% human and 15% D-Bee, with most of the least human looking D-Bees serving in M Brigade. Approximately 15% of the firefighters are literate, 33% are trained paramedics, 2% are Psychic Healers, and all know basic first aid.

5. Robert Street

Robert Street is not his real name, but it will do. Robert is a small time, human dealer in illegal books and antiquities. Nothing big, mostly common stuff, but once in a while he scores big. The Coalition authorities know about Bob (they insist on calling him "Bob"), but ignore him most of the time. However, when something big is going down, they corner Street (he prefers to be called "Street") and shake him down for information. They also raid his place from time to time to see if he's hiding anything dangerous or valuable. They raid his home or shake him down whenever something the Coalition States wants is said to be circulating on the streets. He probably won't have it, but Street may know who does or who the most likely candidates are. Though not technically a stool pigeon, Street is not a brave man and the Coalition authorities know which buttons to push to get Street to give up the goods and tell them what they want to know. Nobody knows how much Street squeals when his feet are put to the fire, so he is not disliked or distrusted by his underworld compatriots. However, most of Street's contemporaries consider him to be a strictly "small time nobody" barely worth their time or attention. That means he doesn't have many connections in high places and even his lowly ones don't give him a lot of respect. That having been said, Street keeps his ear to the ground and knows a lot more than people give him credit for, the CS included. Consequently, he gives up a lot less than the CS could get out of him, and the scoundrel is more cagey and brave than people suspect. Furthermore, a lot of the local street people, other two-bit hoods and City Rats know and like Street. Because of this, they regard him as one of their own and will come to him with goods, and offer a helping hand when they can. They may not be powerful or the sharpest pencils in the box, but they are legion. One of these days, Street could very well have the score of a lifetime fall into his lap, and with Tolkeen's downfall, that could be soon.

Adventure Hooks: Just a few possibilities, Street could be involved in any number of scams and schemes in the 'Burbs, provided they involve smuggling, hiding, and fencing contraband, particularly books, disks, artifacts and magic items.

1. Street learns the location of something that will make him a fortune (pre-Rifts or Tolkeen artifacts; could be magic, technology, weapons, ancient books or disks, etc.). Problem is, he knows the CS will be coming to shake him down soon, and will probably keep an eye on him for a few weeks. Besides, he doesn't have the skills or resources to get "it." However, Street digs out his secret savings to hire an adventurer group he thinks he can trust to get him the treasure. Pay is low but fair, plus the clever man promises the group a 20% cut of whatever he can fence it for, and he assures them it will be a considerable amount. Word on the street is that Robert Street is a dealer who can be trusted, so if they deliver, he will too. Their share should be at least 50,000 credits, possibly two or three times that. Obviously the group he hires should be the *player characters*, and if they have a friendly relationship with any of the kids from Camp Firetown, Street will know about them.

This scenario can get complicated if there is a rival group after the treasure, or if the CS catches wind of the expedition and quietly follows behind, waiting to show themselves only after the group recovers the artifact(s). In addition, there could be an unknown defense, guardian or danger protecting or shielding the item(s). Or perhaps a gang of mercs, bandits, practitioners of magic, Retribution Squad, or adventurers who might have stumbled across it first, or shortly after the group gets there, and insists it is theirs to take. Getting the loot (there might be more than one key item of value) back could be a problem.

2. Street purchases something of great value for cheap. The seller didn't know what he had, Street wasn't sure either when he bought it, but everybody wants it – the CS wants it, private collectors will pay a fortune for it (at least half a million), the Black Market and/or the Federation of Magic wants it by whatever means necessary (will pay double whatever the perceived street value is) and maybe it could help a good cause in the right (probably poor) hands. Problem is, Street has learned what the item is and exactly what it can do, so on top of everything else, he wants to make sure it goes to a good home and liquidate it before anybody realizes he has it.

In the alternative, Street knows he must have the item and may even know what it does and how much it is worth, but has no idea what it looks like (and neither does anyone else), so he doesn't know which item in a pile of (4D4x10) items he recently purchased it might be. How does he figure it out? What is it? Who gets it? Who figures out he has it (by backtracking the footsteps of the now dead or tortured, gentle D-Bee who sold a "bunch of junk," to him)? Ah, that is the stuff of adventure.

3. Unknown to the CS and most others, Street has an excellent, ongoing relationship with the child-thieves and City Rats of the Camp Firetown Orphanage. He is something of a kindly mentor to them and a street buddy. They provide him with free information, news, rumors, and general assistance, and he regularly donates 20-30% of whatever he makes from that info. He also does the kids favors, buys them candy, soft drinks, and toys, gets them electronics at cost, talks and plays games with them, and frequently covers up for them to keep them out of trouble, even if it gets him into (a little bit of) hot water. All of this is done out of genuine friendship and kindness, which has earned Street (the kids always call him "Street," out of respect) the kids' lasting loyalty. Most would consider doing almost anything for the man, not that he would ever ask them to do anything really dangerous. Street genuinely cares about the Camp children, especially his secret, street urchin pals. The Coalition doesn't know about them (nor does anyone else) and it is a secret Street will take to his grave before ratting them out. Street will also come to their aid or rescue should any of them get into serious trouble and may hire or trick adventurers to help him/them or do the real dirty work for him while he takes all the credit.

Robert Street Quick Stats

Street is a reasonably happy and smart guy, who became disillusioned with the life of a scholar. One day he decided if he was to be branded a criminal simply because of his education and knowledge, then he'd step over the line and become one. Not a violent or evil individual, Street became an underground dealer in what he knew best, contraband books and pre-Rifts artifacts. Over the years, he has added magic and other contraband, but avoids drugs and weapons, and physically large items. He has done reasonably well for himself in his one-man operation, but is small time compared to the Black Market and many others. He talks about making one big score so he can retire and move away, but he likes the excitement of the 'Burbs, loves the orphans at Camp Firetown, and this 'Burb has been his home his entire life. Truth is, he'd buy a nicer place, or fix up the one he's living in, conduct a little illegal book trade business on the side, and become the Camp's biggest supporter, maybe even teach there (or on the side).

Real Name: Robert Stanislov.

Aliases: Robert Street, Street, and Stan Robertson.

Alignment: Anarchist, with strong leanings toward Unprincipled, and a soft spot for orphans.

Attributes: I.Q. 13, M.E. 14, M.A. 12, P.S. 9, P.P. 10, P.E. 12, P.B. 9, Spd. 21

Hit Points: 32 and **S.D.C.:** 14.

Weight: 200 pounds (90 kg). **Height:** 5 feet, 8 inches (1.75 m).
Age: 49 and looks every bit his age. **P.P.E.:** 7.

Disposition: A hard working dreamer who insists he is a realist. In truth, a hard life and many disappointments have disillusioned Street about life, people, honor and nobility in general, and the Coalition States in particular. However, while he sometimes talks tough and pretends to be a gruff pragmatist, he still puts his faith in a lot of people he knows. He also loves children, especially orphans, tries to help others when he can, is reasonably honest, and dreams about making the one "big score" that will enable him to retire. If not for his low-end criminal life, love of books and history (which makes him a criminal in the eyes of the CS) and the thieves and cutthroats he associates with to conduct business, he would probably be a productive, lawful citizen (and an Unprincipled alignment). Ironically, Street is, in his own frumpy, down to earth way, everything he's disillusioned about, not that he can see it: peace-loving, honorable, noble, trustworthy, well intentioned, open to new ideas and tolerant of different life forms, and tries not to deliberately hurt anybody.

Experience Level: 7th level Rogue Scholar and dealer in contraband books, relics and stolen goods.

Magic Knowledge: Only lore and book knowledge.

Psionics: None.**Attacks per Melee:** Five.

Bonuses: +2 to parry, +2 to dodge, +2 to roll with impact, +2 to pull punch, kick attack does 1D6 S.D.C.

Skills of Note: Basically a Rogue Scholar turned antiquities street dealer and petty crook. Speaks and is literate in American, Spanish, and Dragonese, all at 98%, Writing 80%, Basic Math 90%, Anthropology 65%, Art 90%, Cook 80%, Computer Operation 95% Computer Programming 85%, Cryptography 65%, Radio: Basic 90%, TV & Video 63%, Concealment 48%, Intelligence 50%, Law 80%, Lore: Demons & Monster 75%, Pick Locks 65%, Palming 55%, Pilot Hovercraft 95%, Pilot Automobile 84%, Pilot Jet Pack 80%, Prowl 60%, Streetwise 48%, Running, Swimming 85%, and Hand to Hand: Basic.

Weapon Proficiencies: W.P. Automatic Pistol (S.D.C.) and W.P. Energy Pistol, both at 7th level proficiency.

Weapons & Armor: Has a suit of Urban Warrior armor (50 M.D.C.), a small Vibro-Knife (1D4 M.D.), a Wilk's 237 "Backup" laser pistol (3D6 M.D. per single blast, 6D6 M.D. per double pulse, 500 foot/152 m range, 16 single shot or 8 double shot clip payload, and +2 to strike on an aimed shot), a Triax TX-20 "Short" laser pistol (2D6 M.D., 800 foot/244 m range, 20 shot clip, and is easy to conceal; he won it in a game of cards), and a 10 mm automatic pistol (5D6 S.D.C., 20 shot clip, 200 foot/61 m range); four ammo clips for each weapon. He has access to other weapons and gear, but has no need for them.

Money: 1D6x1000 Universal Credits on him at any time, 40,000 credits in a local bank, and another 25,000 credits buried along with roughly 30 forbidden books and an extra Backup laser pistol and two E-Clips in a secret place away from home.

Description: Street is just plain folk, a burly leather-faced human with a tinkle in his warm brown eyes. His hair is light brown with streaks of grey, and he usually dresses in plain articles of clothing dirty from roaming the streets. He cheats at gambling only when he's confident he won't get caught, and rips off Coalition citizens and authorities whenever he can, otherwise, his word is his bond and he can be trusted.

6. The home of Sebastian Shock

Sebastian Shock is the owner of *S&S Pictures and Frames*, an art store, frame shop and gallery, but on the street he is reputed to be a (not so) retired smuggler and forger. The home is nothing special on the outside, except for the painted-over Mega-Damage doors and bars on the windows. Inside is a different story. The house is super clean, neat, and as posh as they get in the 'Burbs. A state of the art electronic security system protects the owner and the home's contents. Furnishings are plush and expensive, the high-tech entertainment systems, electronics and computers are of the best brands and latest models, the master bedroom opulent. Like most of the homes in Firetown, there is indoor plumbing, hot and cold running water, and electric lights. However, Sebby, as his friends call him, has a private generator out back in case of power outages, central air conditioning, a forced air heating system and private well. The basement is a Mega-Damage bunker with a spare bedroom, game room (pool table, big screen TV, disk player and electronic arcade games), but here again, there is nothing to hint of illegal activity or contraband. His 500 video disks are *all* legal and his computer files clean as a whistle. The home can be swept and gone over with a fine tooth comb by CS troops without unearthing anything illegal or the least bit incriminating. The only thing one can say about "Sebby" is that he likes to hang out with unsavory characters: Adventurers, City Rats, known underworld figures, prostitutes and dance hall girls – but poor choices in friends is not a crime even to the CS and Sebby makes no bones about living an exciting and "wee bit decadent" lifestyle.

Adventure Hooks: 1. Though the CS has never been able to prove it, word on the street is that Sebastian Shock is one of the very best (and smartest) forgers and smugglers in the business, and is most definitely *not* retired. Part of what makes him so good is that he masterminds and orchestrates everything but takes a direct hand in nothing. When people come to him with "a problem" he directs them to "a friend" who *may* be able to help them out. That friend, of course, is a forger, smuggler, fence, Black Market agent, mercenary, assassin, professional thief, City Rat, Cyber-Doc, plastic surgeon, practitioner of magic, scholar, specialty dealer, crook or other *free agent* who specializes in solving particular problems. According to the street grapevine, Sebby knows everybody who is anybody in the criminal underworld operating in the 'Burbs of *Firetown, Mayhem* and *New Colfax*. So if a player character has "a problem" or is looking for "something special" (i.e., illegal contraband), Sebby can, probably, fix them up. Likewise, Sebby can put freelancers, adventurers, D-Bees and even practitioners of magic looking for work in touch with "the right people." Presumably, Sebby gets a kickback from every "referral," but there are many who suspect he is actually a kingpin in the Black Market. Exactly how big or high up he may be, or if the speculation is even true, remains a mystery.

Note: This makes the Sebastian Shock character a wonderful reappearing Non-Player Character in any ongoing 'Burbs campaign or setting where the Chi-Town 'Burbs are the adventurers' base of operation. However, player characters should *never* think of this criminal mastermind as a true friend or ally. Despite appearances, Sebby does everything for a reason, usually a financial reward, a favor he can call upon or a valuable connection for the future. If he has to turn somebody in to the CS to save his own backside or to advance his own agenda he does so without the slightest hesitation.

Sebastian Shock Quick Stats

Sebastian Shock, himself, comes off as a confident, sleazy individual who half-pretends to be an honest businessman but seems more like the Cheshire Cat from Alice in Wonderland. He always has at least one beautiful woman on his arm, often two or three, is an infamous womanizer and loves to party, throwing gatherings and events at his home and at rented halls and nightclubs. In fact, Sebby spends 90% of his time socializing and partying, leaving his business, S & S Pictures and Frames, in the capable hands of his manager and employees.

Sebby has never been known to threaten or attack anybody, let alone kill. In fact, very few people can ever remember him raising his voice even under the most tense situations – Mr. Shock always seems to be calm, confident, smiling and unafraid. Being who he is and who he hangs out with (the criminal underworld, adventurers and fugitives), Sebby is always surrounded by a posse of 12-36 "friends and associates," several of whom function as his personal bodyguards. He *never* hires bodyguards himself, somehow they are just always present.

Real Name: Henry Collins Quin.

Aliases: Steven Smith, Sebastian Shock, Mr. Shock, and Sebby. While he encourages "friends" to call him Sebby, people can only do so after he asks them to. If a stranger walks up out of the Blue and calls him "Sebby," he will snap his fingers or glance at one of his bodyguards and a trio of them will escort the stranger to the street where they'll give him a few punches, kicks and a toss into the dirt.

Alignment: Miscreant evil.

Attributes: I.Q. 24, M.E. 19, M.A. 22, P.S. 9, P.P. 14, P.E. 10, P.B. 11, Spd. 10

Hit Points: 61. **S.D.C.:** 24.

Weight: 200 pounds (90 kg). **Height:** 6 feet (1.8 m). **Age:** 46 (looks 34).

P.P.E.: 9

Disposition: Cool, calm and supremely confident with the cool demeanor of a cobra who can mesmerize you with his charm and strike you down before you know what hit you. Sebby is perpetually charming, smiling and content. Nothing seems to get under his skin, and he always has a bit of wry wit or an amusing retort for every situation. His calm confidence is scary, leaving many who meet him to wonder what's really going on behind those twinkling eyes and his serpentine smile. He is this way even when discussing life and death situations.

Sebby is a master planner, strategist and organizer who can see the big picture and nine times out of ten, be ready for every possible contingency, thus nothing throws him. When that one out of ten happens, so far he has been able to think on his feet to pull victory out of defeat or to cut his losses (usually sacrificing others) with no or minimal losses.

Insanities: Sebastian Shock is a narcissistic megalomaniac with delusions of absolute superiority. Though it doesn't show, he thrives on action, intrigue and excitement. If there wasn't a chance he'd get caught or lose part of his criminal empire,

there would be no fun in what he does, and he lives for the challenge. He delights in outwitting all comers and knows he is better than everybody else, so much better that nobody even suspects how rich or powerful he really is. His exterior calm is just a mask. His chosen method of operation is to be the invisible mover and shaker behind the scenes. The wheels in his head are always spinning with new schemes and up to the second reassessments. What makes him so good, besides being a genius and his ability to think on his feet and manipulate others, is he has learned to accept his (very few) limitations. Thus, he (usually) doesn't overreach, act on emotion or do anything foolish. He is so comfortable with the image he has built for himself that his secret life as a criminal mastermind means everything, and he loves every minute of it. As for other weaknesses, Sebby coyly admits he has "a taste for colorful characters and a weakness for beautiful women, but who doesn't." In truth, it's all part of his narcissism, power games and thrill seeking.

Experience Level: 12th level Smuggler and crime lord.

Magic Knowledge: Only lore and rumors about people.

Attacks per Melee: Six.

Bonuses: +1 on initiative, +2 to strike, +3 to parry, +3 to dodge, +4 to roll with impact, +4 to pull punch, kick attack does 1D6 S.D.C., +2 to save vs psionic attack, and 70% to evoke trust or intimidate.

Skills of Note: Includes the +10% skill bonus for a high I.Q. Speaks American, Spanish, and Techno-Can, all at 98%, literate in American/English 98%, Basic and Advanced Math 98%, Radio: Basic 98%, Radio: Scramblers 98%, Cryptography 98%, Detect Ambush 98%, Detect Concealment 98%, Disguise 98%, Concealment 88%, Palming 98%, Streetwise 88%, Find Contraband 98%, Escape Artist 98, Computer Operation 98%, Computer Programming 98%, Computer Hacking 80%, Law 98%, Lore: Magic 80%, Pilot Hover Vehicles 98%, Pilot Hovercycle 98%, Pilot Motorcycle 98%, Pilot Motorboats 85%, and Hand to Hand: Basic.

Weapon Proficiencies: W.P. Energy Pistol and W.P. Knife, both at 12th level proficiency.

Weapons & Armor: Wears fashionable suits made of light M.D.C. fabric (16 M.D.C.) and has bodyguards nearby to shield him and to throw on an additional M.D.C. armored trench coat (26 M.D.C. with plating over key areas; the latest offering by the Black Market for those who need to be fashionable). When he knows he's heading into a potentially volatile situation, Sebastian wears an illegal force field belt of alien origin. It provides 200 M.D.C. with the press of a button. Additionally, Sebby is so skilled at slipping it on and off, palming it and slipping it to one of his bodyguards, that no one knows he owns it.

Bodyguards: Typically, all six to twelve are 6-8th level protectors in a variety of O.C.C.s. A basic, small group includes one Juicer (Sebby finds Crazies too annoying for him), two professional assassins (women), one full conversion 'Borg that looks completely human (female), one other heavy, full conversion 'Borg, and a psychic, preferably a Mind Melter, Psi-Slayer or Nega-Psychic. A larger group will include 2-4 Headhunters or other warrior types, another psychic or two and a practitioner of magic (spell caster); half are women.

Remember, Sebby never actually hires these people though they always meet with his taste and approval. If questioned by the authorities, Sebby says something like, "Apparently, one of my friends or acquaintances thought I was in need of protection. Thankfully, I have many concerned friends to watch out for me. Darling of them to be so concerned, isn't it?" **Note:** Mr. Shock is famous for never having harmed the hair on the head of any living being, at least not personally. That's what his bodyguards, friends and associates are for, and even then Sebby never gives out a direct order to harm or kill anybody.

Cybernetics: Built-in language translator, head jack, amplified hearing, sound filtration system, sound identifier, radio bandit's ear, lung: toxic filter, lung: oxygen storage cell, gyro-compass, and clock calendar. See **Rifts® Bionics Sourcebook** for descriptions of them all; the **Rifts® RPG** also has most.

Money: Sebby has 6D6x1000 credits and wears 90,000 credits worth of jewelry on him at any time. He has another 120,000 credits in the *Firetown Universal Bank*, his home and the contents inside are worth a collective 1.5 million credits (the M.D.C. features is what jacks up the value), and his Pictures and Frame shop business grosses one million annually. That's his legitimate and apparent worth. On the Black Market who knows. If he is the big player some people think he is, Sebby could be worth 100-600 million credits, maybe more! Part of it safely tucked away in Black Market banking facilities, part stashed in places outside the CS and part of it invested. Speaking of which, rumor has it that Sebby owns a mansion, and a Juicer and a Bionics conversion shop in the independent kingdom of *Kingsdale*, and who knows what else.

Description: A thin, fairly good looking fellow who appears to be thirty-something. He has a full crop of black hair, always dress impeccably in expensive clothes, wears jewelry, has a beautiful woman (or two) hanging on his arm and he smiles most of the time. A half dozen to a dozen (unofficial) bodyguards are part of his entourage and image.

7. David Darklighter

Nobody knows exactly what David Darklighter does or how he makes his living. He is said to be an adventurer or explorer though others claim he is a Rogue Scientist, and some that he is a practitioner of magic. Whatever the guy is, he tends to stick to himself, and stay in his home. As an adventurer, Darklighter is often away for months at a time. He has recently returned from an 18 month sojourn and is worse for the wear. Those who saw him limp into town say his face and hands were scarred and he is minus his left leg just below the hip. He has been holed up in his home, calling out for deliveries of food and supplies. His damaged appearance a week or so after the final siege on the cities of Tolkeen and Freehold has started the rumor mills cranking out stories that Darklighter is indeed a sorcerer recently returned from the Tolkeen war front. He currently refuses to take visitors, not that he has any (known) friends in town, and has locked himself indoors.

Adventure Hooks: 1. Curious youngsters, perhaps from one of the orphanages, have been spying on Darklighter, perhaps even sneaking into his home where they saw . . . what? Game Master, this is your chance to go with any number of storylines involving this mysterious figure. Here are a few ideas, some of which could be combined:

a) Saw a pair of demons but no sign of the man. Could he be a Shifter? If so, what is he up to? Are the demons protectors or minions? Or could they be looking for Darklighter? If so, why and where is Darklighter?

b) Saw him talking to three or more hooded figures, couldn't hear everything, but they were saying something about "Tolkeen," "the CS must be made to pay" and "striking at Chi-Town before they are completely prepared." Is Darklighter a Tolkeen supporter? Is he a member of a Tolkeen Retribution Squad? Is the 'Burb in danger?

c) Saw him arguing with three or more shadowy figures, couldn't hear everything, but Darklighter was saying he "had enough of killing," "will not participate," "don't threaten him," and that they should leave. The only clear thing one of the other men was heard saying is, "Don't interfere with this" and "you're either with us or against us." What's this about?

d) Saw Darklighter weeping and asking God to forgive him. A handgun was on an end table nearby. Regret for past deeds? Considering suicide? Or is something terrible about to be unleashed/happen?

e) Found Darklighter in his basement burning books and computer disks. What's that all about?

f) Saw Darklighter hiding a small metal box, sealed with wax, in a secret place in the floor. They went back later, after the man was asleep, but they couldn't find the secret compartment where they thought it was. Maybe they're mistaken. Don't know what was in the box. Mean anything?

g) Darklighter wasn't there, but they heard strange sounds and creaking floorboards like somebody walking. When the lights came on and a door opened, but nobody was there, the kids bolted. They are convinced Darklighter's home is haunted.

2. If Darklighter is recently returned from Tolkeen is trouble following him? What kind, Coalition, Retribution Squad or demonic? Did he return with any souvenirs, like magic artifacts or weapons, or treasure? Local thieves are asking themselves that same question right now. The CS don't seem to care or haven't heard the rumors.

3. A half naked, dead body is found laying in an alley or in Greenleaf Park. In his clenched fist is a crumpled piece of paper with Darklighter's address. He's an outsider nobody knows. Looks like an adventurer or maybe a merc judging from his muscles and scars. The body has been looted (probably by locals) so it's hard to tell anything else about the deceased. Puzzling is the fact that he appears to have been electrocuted (magically?). If questioned and shown photos of the dead man, Darklighter claims not to know him or to have any idea why he may have had his address. Could this be a thief or assassin dispatched by Darklighter and dumped away from his house? If an assassin, who's out to get Darklighter and why? The CS still doesn't care even if told about the rumors and dead man. Is this just typical CS disinterest or is there some other reason? Could Darklighter be one of their agents or freelancers? If so, he probably isn't a sorcerer of any kind. Psychic, scout or assassin, perhaps?

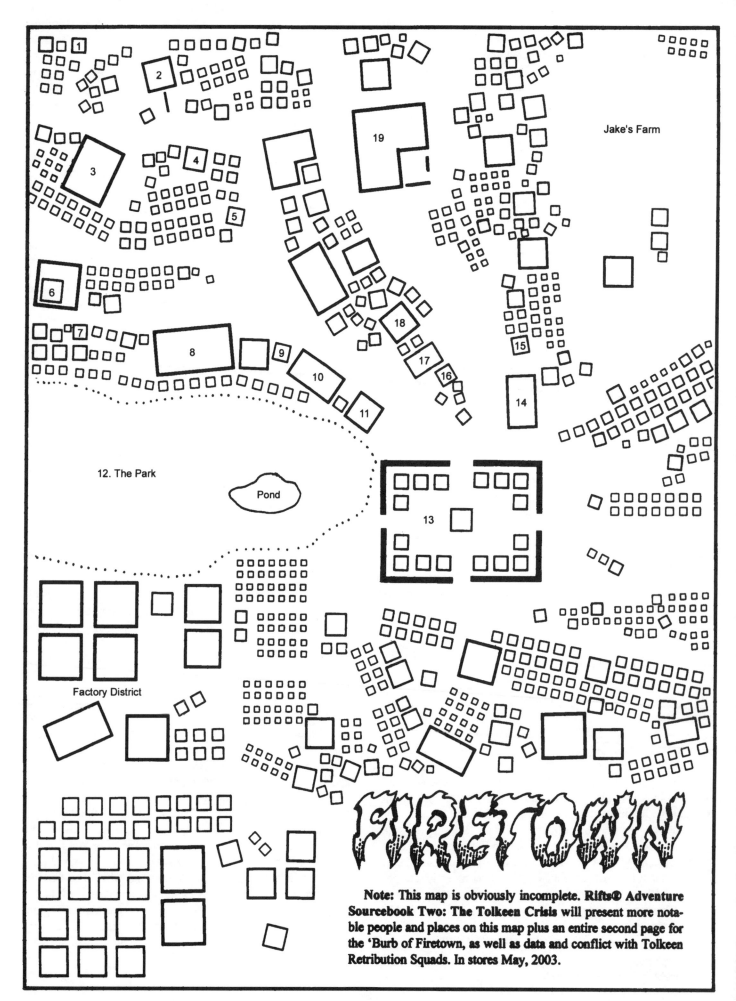

Jake's Farm

19

18
17
16
15
14

3
4
5
6
7
8
9
10
11
1
2

12. The Park

Pond

13

Factory District

FIRETOWN

Note: This map is obviously incomplete. **Rifts® Adventure Sourcebook Two: The Tolkeen Crisis** will present more notable people and places on this map plus an entire second page for the 'Burb of Firetown, as well as data and conflict with Tolkeen Retribution Squads. In stores May, 2003.

4. Darklighter is found dead (or has gone missing), his home broken into and torn apart as if the perpetrators were looking for something. Other broken furniture and articles suggest they were smashed in rage – perhaps frustration that they could not find whatever it is they were looking for (or that Darklighter got away)?

Note: No stats for this NPC so the G.M. can make him anything he or she may want. Just because the street grapevine thinks Darklighter is a sorcerer doesn't mean he is one. Such talk could be a red herring, a false lead or distraction to what's really going on, and Darklighter could be a good guy or evil, or an absolute nobody who has become mysterious simply because he is a loner and the completely unsubstantiated gossip has sprung up as a result.

8. Parkview Hotel

A fairly new but dingy looking, four story hotel. It has 320 rooms, six suites, an exercise room, swimming pool and eight small conference rooms, one large. There is no onsite restaurant, but there are a few good ones nearby, with Park Place getting the highest recommendation. A parking structure for the hotel is next door. An average room costs 65 credits a night, a high-end room 100, and a luxury suite 200 credits (can comfortably accommodate 6-8 guests sleeping over).

Adventure Hooks: Hotels can be the meeting place and source of all kinds of intrigue. The very nature of a hotel makes them an anonymous meeting place for illicit affairs, sex, prostitution, gambling, drug buys, illegal bionic augmentation, abortions, buying or selling contraband, drop-offs and exchanges of (legal and illegal) goods and services of every conceivable possibility, to parties, reunions, business meetings, contract negotiations, romantic getaways and innocent get togethers.

Guests may include out-of-towners, vacationers, families, teenagers, priests, business people, scholars, the homeless who happened to scrounge enough cash to stay a night or two, refugees, fugitives, prostitutes, drug dealers, gamblers, smugglers, thieves, killers, weapon dealers, bounty hunters, mercenaries, adventurers, practitioners of magic, monsters, D-Bees, Coalition soldiers, CS spies, CS citizens slumming or on an adventure, and scores of others. Use these diverse people and the anonymous setting as the backdrop of numerous rendezvous, meetings, intrigue and skullduggery.

9. Park Lane Bakery

Yummy cakes, pies, cookies, pastries, bread and snacks at very reasonable prices; pies are among the high priced items at 4-6 credits a pie (good for 8-10 slices) and whole cakes cost 6-10 credits depending on the size and decorations. Also sells fruit juices, milk, tea and coffee by the glass and by the quart; 1-3 credits each. A popular place for locals, visitors from the hotel and shoppers at the nearby Barter's Square and stores across the street.

Adventure Hooks: 1. Park Lane Bakery is a regular hangout with a couple dozen kids from the Camp Fireplace Orphanage. There are a few reasons for this: One, the owner and most of the bakers use the orphans to make short delivery runs and do simple chores or little favors and the pay the kids in bread, cookies and pastries, sometimes a whole pie or cake. The orphans also keep a lookout for shoplifters. They never steal from the bakery, so it is a happy, win, win situation for all parties involved. Two, the City Rats and other orphan street kids can pick up on current news, rumors and gossip from the many patrons who come and go all day long. Three, the child-thieves can sometimes pick an easy pocket, snatch items hanging out of a purse or bag, and bat their big eyelashes and get the occasional handout. This also means the orphans may recognize public figures, criminals and others who come to the shop.

2. The City Rats and street urchins from Camp Fireplace might also bring trouble to the bakery from time to time. For example, several of them hide stolen items and cherished personal items on the premises. If some thug or victim of theirs is looking for them, they might follow the kids to the bakery. Or if a kid gets caught trying to pinch a wallet or steal a pastry out of a customer's shopping bag, there could be trouble.

Otherwise, the owners and the workers keep their noses clean and stay out of trouble.

10. Park Place Restaurant

Location, location, location is what helps to make the Park Place Restaurant a busy, around the clock, establishment. It is located at a junction where Greenleaf Park is its backyard, the Parkview Hotel is a short walk down the street, the pharmacy is next door, the bustling Barter's Square is across the way, a mini-shopping district is on the opposite street and the Bunker Nightclub is two streets over, not to mention the local residents and factory workers, all of which send a constant crowd of hungry patrons their way.

The Park Place is really more like two businesses in one, the family restaurant on the main floor and the Park Gentlemen's Club on the second floor.

The first floor is the **Park Place Family Restaurant**. It is open to the mainstream public and offers a wide range of dining selections. Everything from soups, meatloaf, steaks, lamb, fish and chicken dinners to sandwiches, french fries, breakfast foods (available anytime of the day) and a selection of desserts (half of them purchased from the Park Lane Bakery). Prices are fair to low, 5-10 credits for the average meal depending on what it is, non-alcoholic drinks 1-2 credits, and a choice of six beers and four different wines at 2-4 credits a glass. All the food here is good to very good and the service is quick and friendly. The restaurant is usually packed at breakfast, lunch and dinner time till about 10 o'clock at night when it thins out to about half and then to one third of the patrons after midnight. A downstairs hall can be rented for family functions, receptions, birthdays and meetings for 60 credits a day (ends at 6:00 p.m.) or night (from 7:00 pm till 1:00 a.m.) on slow weekdays, or for 200 credits on the busy days, Thursday through Sunday. Catering is an additional cost charged by the plate.

The second floor is the **Park Gentlemen's Club & Fine Dining**, also known on the streets as the "G-Club." It is reserved for Firetown's business people, wealthy and elite, and though it is call a "gentlemen's club," women are just as welcome. There is a dress code (suits and ties optional if the clothes are expensive, elegant and fashionable) and a 500 credit cover charge per person (that's in addition to the meal and drinks) for visitors not known by the maitre d' or manager, or who are not "guests" of a regular patron. This is to keep out the riffraff and sightseers. Reservations are required, ideally two days in advance, and a walk-in off the street is usually looking at a 1-4 hour wait, and sometimes there are no available tables any time of the day or night. This happens when several groups reserve part of the restaurant for parties, gatherings and meetings.

Where the downstairs family restaurant is bright, noisy and tables are packed close together, the ambiance of the Club is dark, quiet and luxurious. A full-service bar offers a huge range of alcoholic drinks and a wonderful wine list, a pianist plays softly in the corner and a pair of waiters present the five or seven course dinners to each table, waiting on the diners hand and foot. In addition to the open dining area, there are six private dining/meeting rooms that seat up to 12 people (cost 1000 credits an hour) and eight intimate dining rooms for 2-4 people (cost 600 credits an hour). For those who enjoy such pleasures, there is an after dinner smoking lounge where patrons can relax, light up and order drinks. The hidden upstairs kitchen, the wine room, security office, the owner's spacious office and a private apartment (the owner's, but often rented out to special patrons) are also found secluded away on the second floor.

The cost of an *average meal* is 150-200 credits, plus drinks and dessert (both cost about 5-15 credits per drink or serving). Of course, part of what one is paying for is the atmosphere and security. Nobody knows how it's been accomplished, but the CS authorities have *never* raided the club and give it a wide berth. Presumably, somebody has been paid off, but to pull this off, that "somebody" must be very high up in the CS military and ISS police totem poles.

Security to keep the Park Gentlemen's Club exclusive and safe for the rich and powerful, is invisible. Some look like wait staff or maitre d's, others like diners out for a quiet evening. They include a tap dancing Dog Boy named Rulf dressed as a maitre d' (8th level), a Psi-Tech named Lola dressed as high society femme fatale (6th level; P.B. 22), a Psi-Nullifier named Bruce dressed as a businessman (9th level, and usually accompanies Lola), a Zapper named Sparky, dressed as a lounge singer (7th level and has a great singing voice), an ebony skinned Ley Line Walker named Tyrone, dressed in a white tuxedo and posing as one of the club's two photographers (7th level), and lastly, a cyborg called Doorstop. He is a full conversion 'Borg armed with a battery of weapons ideal for close combat and subduing party crashers. He stands in one particular corner so still and quiet that many patrons think he is a statue. He is so motionless because he is jacked into the entire security surveillance system where he simultaneously monitors eight security cameras and radio chatter between the other members of the security team. Doorstop takes action only when necessary. There are six additional 4-6 level security personnel, half female, all experts in the art of hand to hand combat (any Man at Arms O.C.C. skilled in close combat) and one Air Warlock and one Ley Line Walker (both 5th level) on staff in a private security office. They come out only when needed or asked to address a situation. Furthermore, concealed electronics scan for explosives, cameras, and recording and listening devices, none of which are allowed in the club.

The Park Gentlemen's Club is so safe that crime lords and big shots throughout the Chi-Town 'Burbs come to dine and hold meetings. Even the occasional Chi-Town hot shot makes an appearance, but most CS citizens know to stay away from the club.

Adventure Hooks: Wherever the wealthy, powerful and criminal elite go, secret deals, trades, meetings and skullduggery are sure to follow.

1. All kinds of top secret meetings, hand-offs, and deal making go on here. Run with it.

2. All kinds of top criminal kingpins dine and hold private meetings here. It is one of Sebastian Shock's favorite places, so he can be found here most evenings around 7:00-10:00 p.m. before he goes nightclub hopping.

3. All kinds of underworld meetings and transactions take place in the quiet of the G-Club, as it is called in certain circles. To infiltrate or bust one up is to risk one's life. Troublemakers at the club have a nasty habit of disappearing. **Note:** While raiding the club may border on the impossible (or the insane), staking out the back door, streets, and the downstairs restaurant are easy. This could be a good place to spot and then follow an underground figure.

4. Rumor: The owner, an elusive man by the name of Kalrisian Blue, who lives in a mansion in *Prosekville,* is really a powerful adult dragon who spent decades adventuring and making connections. Exactly why he has settled down in the Chi-Town 'Burbs, what his personal agenda may be, and what ties he has, if any, to the Black Market or criminal underworld are unknown. This could explain another rumor that the G-Club is protected by a Sanctum spell and other protective magicks. If

the CS should get *evidence* that this rumor is true, their hands-off policy *might* come to a swift end and the Park Gentlemen's Club shut down or the entire building torn down after a thorough search of the premises.

5. Rumor: The most powerful and valuable magic items and pre-Rifts artifacts are sold and hand delivered at the G-Club. In fact, Mr. Blue is said to have quite a collection himself. Likewise, big payoffs for other contraband and drugs are also said to take place at the club.

6. Rumor: Kalrisian Blue is really a Coalition spy and the G-Club an incredibly well crafted and complex scheme to observe (and undermine) the criminal underworld and anti-Coalition factions. This would certainly explain why the Coalition authorities stay away, but could it really be true?

11. Park Pharmacy & General Store

An all purpose, above the boards pharmacy and general store that sells everything from greeting cards, scotch tape and cosmetics, to basic grocery items, snack foods, alcohol and over the counter vitamins and medicines. Includes a 30 terminal cyber-café on the second floor that taps into the Chi-Town internet. Prices are standard.

Adventure Hooks: Nothing cosmic, this one's a typical Walgreens style pharmacy. Shoplifting, the occasional armed robbery, parking lot mugging and bounty hunter snatch job is about as exciting as things get.

12. Greenleaf Park

This used to be an old city dump, but it has been covered over, cleaned and turned into a nice park with low rolling hills, cut lawn, trees, flowers, small pond, park benches, walking trail, bike path and sidewalk vendors (peanuts, popcorn, hot dogs, ice cream, and refreshments). It is reasonably safe and populated during the day, though there are rowdy groups of children, mouthy punks, beggars, homeless, City Rats and the occasional street gang hanging at the park. Local authorities patrol the grounds and so do a couple of citizen groups, keeping it pretty safe and

clean. Scores of factory workers also come to the park to eat their lunch and to grab a smoke or some fresh air during break periods and to chat for a while after work.

At night, it's a different story. Police patrols stop after midnight and that's when trouble visits Greenleaf in the form of vice, violence, crime and stupidity. At night, the nocturnal predators come out, and Greenleaf Park is one of their hunting grounds. Roving bands of City Rats, gangs of street punks and Cyber-Snatchers, gang wars, drug dealing, buying or trading contraband, prostitution in the bushes, duels, and random acts of violence and stupidity all take place in the park. Things are especially bad in the Spring, Summer and Fall when the weather is at its nicest, but these sorts of things occur in the Winter too. A hundred or more homeless people also make their homes in the park, arriving as it gets dark and finding a place to sleep on park benches and under trees. Residents and street smart individuals know to stay out of the park unless they are looking for drugs, contraband or trouble. Visitors aren't so bright and may stumble onto trouble in complete ignorance.

Adventure Hooks: These are just a few ideas.

1. Any of the encounters suggested above.

2. The late-night meeting. So and so said to meet him in Greenleaf Park at 1:00 a.m.

3. The safe public meeting. A daytime meeting when and where plenty of people are around as witnesses to any acts of foul play.

4. The romantic rendezvous (perhaps really a trap for a mugging, a kidnaping, cyber-snatching, etc.).

5. Someone or something is killing hookers or homeless people in the park. What does it mean and does anybody care?

6. One of the player characters is challenged to a duel in Greenleaf Park, or the group is challenged to a rumble in the park (may or may not be a fight to the death).

7. A man is found slain in the park, nothing new there, only it turns out that he was a notoriously mean Coalition Army officer (or ISS officer). A note taped to the body reads: "One by one the tyranny shall end." Is this the handiwork of one man or some kind of group? This officer had plenty of enemies in the 'Burbs and in the Army. The letter could be a ruse to draw attention away from a military suspect. Or it could be a group of D-Bees or Burbies tired of this man and his crew's brutality, or the work of a Tolkeen Retribution Squad or agents of the Federation of Magic, or someone else entirely.

The soldiers (or police) who served under this officer are equally vicious and cruel. They are out for revenge and concerned about finding the person or persons responsible for their own safety. They begin a ruthless campaign of terror to find that individual or group. CS higher ups are not happy when one of their own is killed and give these brutes plenty of latitude in their investigation – Burbies and D-Bees are likely to get hurt and some people will die. Consequently, the local authorities are also looking into the matter and may hire outside investigators (the player group). Is this murder an isolated incident that passes without resolve or is another slain Coalition soldier found a few days later? Is it from the same squad (which might suggest a vendetta against that particular group rather than an attack on the Coalition States or Chi-Town) or is it someone from a different squad? How do the CS loyalists and soldiers who frequent Karl's Revenge take these killings? Do they launch their own vigilante investigation, go on a lynch party, or start beating up innocent D-Bees? (See description #2 for details on this tavern and its patrons.)

8. Gang violence at night is spilling into the daytime and causing such a stir the local police may be forced to do something about it. Or to avoid continuing retribution from the gang members' comrades and friends, the police secretly hire a band of adventurers (the player characters) to find and teach the bullies a lesson. If anyone gets killed (gang-bangers or the hired guns) the police are not implicated, and lethal force on the part of the hired adventurers is advised. "These gangs of thieves, murderers and Cyber-Snatchers need to be eradicated," they tell the adventurers. "Don't be shy about using extreme force."

13. Barter Square

Barter Square is a combination outlet mall and giant flea market. There are 16 permanent retail stores and 160 spaces for 4D4x10 independent vendors who buy a display space to pitch their tent or set up tables to hawk whatever it is they have to sell. Every other weekend has a special theme and the non-permanent vendors are required to sell products or services related to that theme. In the center of the Square is a large food court and restroom, with tables for shoppers to sit and eat or rest their tired feet.

The temporary vendors include local businesses looking to sell off extra or old inventory at a discount, traveling merchants, medicine shows, snake oil salesmen, psychic healers, fortune-tellers, Wilderness Scouts and fur traders, adventurers with booty to sell, Psi-Stalkers or Indians (usually selling animal skins, teeth, tusks, jewelry, herbs and blankets) or residents of the 'Burb (and surrounding 'Burbs) looking to sell off a bunch of old junk, flea market style.

Adventure Hooks: Most dealers and temporary sellers are honest, but there a number of con artists, thieves, cheats and scoundrels at every show. A confrontation with them can lead to a brawl, gunfight and even murder.

1. A weapons dealer selling second-hand weapons as new. Half need a thorough cleaning, a third are junk that break after a few weeks of use (and are minus -1 to strike even on an aimed shot), and about a quarter of the weapons in good condition may even be new. Everything is overpriced for what one actually gets, but the seller makes them sound like the deal of the decade and is doing strong business from people who don't know better. This crooked arms dealer will remember anybody who makes a fool of him, criticizes his merchandise or chases away customers. He will take note of them and get even when the opportunity presents itself.

2. Medicine show. This traveling snake oil salesman has a tonic, herbal concoction or ointment for anything that might ail a person. Only 10% have any true medicinal qualities, 80% are alcoholic concoctions passed off as medicine or a drug mixture to make the user high (and hence, feeling no pain) and 10% are completely worthless as medicine or for a drug high. This fast talking weasel is a con man from way back and he has 3-6 teammates working the crowd by offering testimonials, picking pockets and rolling drunks. If somebody challenges or threatens the salesman, his goons (3-6 level thieves and bandits) are on them in a heartbeat.

3. A gem among junk. A shopper (one of the player characters?) accidentally finds something of value, for cheap, in a pile of second-hand junk. It could be a pre-Rifts artifact, an alien weapon, tool, expensive machine part, an alien device, a magic item, a gem, an expensive piece of jewelry, a rare or outlawed book, and so on. Did anyone else notice the purchase? If so, is the character jumped by thieves as he makes his way home, or beset by CS troops looking for contraband, or approached by someone who wants to buy it from him for a profit? Or approached by someone who wants to hire him for a job/adventure, saying anyone who knew what the item was (or wanted one) is the person he is looking to hire.

4. An old enemy. What are the odds of running into an old adversary here?

5. A fugitive or criminal with a price on his head and he or she is all yours for the taking. The only problem is all the innocent people who might get hurt when the fugitive is attacked. And maybe the player character or group isn't the only one to have noticed the desperado. In the alternative, a bounty hunter or Coalition soldier looking to apprehend or destroy a player character or the adventurer group.

6. A player character or the group is on the run and there's no better place to lose someone than in the thronging evening or weekend crowds at Barter's Square.

7. The frightened seller. A scrawny looking teenage boy (or a kid, old lady, housewife, Psi-Stalker, scout, warrior, or whoever) has something to sell in a bundle under his arm. He is obviously nervous, keeps looking over his shoulder and at the people around him. He has walked up to this particular booth three times now in the last 15 minutes, and once even asked if the gent buys "antiques, really old antiques," but has yet to screw-up the courage to show him what he has. One of the player characters could carefully approach the timid teen and strike up a conversation. He'll have to be careful or he'll spook the lad. With some smiles and polite conversation he should be able to get a look at what he has in the bundle. Otherwise, the player character(s) could hang around the booth, looking over his shoulder until the kid reveals his treasure. If the dealer doesn't want it, or if the dealer offers a low price for it, the player character could jump in with a better offer. This can be tricky because if the dealer wants it but was looking for a good deal, it could start a bidding war and earn the dealer's ire (the player character just cost him money or bought the item right out from under his nose). If the dealer is a criminal or evil, the character may have just earned himself an enemy and trouble to come later that day. **Note:** An observant character may be able to spot all kinds of shoppers and sellers who might be looking for more than to buy or sell a few odds and ends. There are those looking to sell items they found or stole and have no idea what they are. There are those who found or stole items the know are contraband but want (or need) to sell them for as much as possible so they come to Barter Square looking to get the best possible price (or best sounding price) they can. They don't care who they sell it to.

8. The promise of forbidden knowledge is what one of the temporary dealers or one of the

shoppers is offering. This individual may be attractive, plain, ugly or sleazy looking, old or young, probably human. He claims to have books and films banned by the CS. Items that he is willing to sell for low prices and which he (or she) is willing to allow prospective customers to examine before buying. All one has to do is meet him at the east entrance and he'll take all interested parties to his "stash." Is this person legitimate or is this come kind of con game? Or is it a sting operation? Are there CS surveillance people taking their pictures or taping their conversation? Is this a sting to flush out dealers and collectors of contraband? Is it a trap or a rare opportunity? Are any of the characters willing to find out?

9. A D-Bee is clutching a stack of (1D6+4) books under his hooded cloak. They are rare and highly valuable items, easily worth 1D4x10,000 credits each. He will only "trade" and wants magic items (perhaps a few very specific items) or to find a particular individual (a reputed sorcerer) or some other dangerous information about Chi-Town or the CS patrols, or the sewers under the city, etc. Do the player characters have what it takes to trade? Is it worth following this little guy to see what he's up to? It's gotta be trouble.

10. Drugs dealers also wander the premises looking for buyers, and pick pockets and thieves keep an eye out for easy marks.

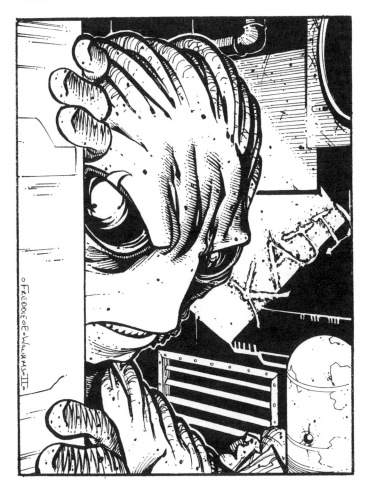

14. The Bunker Nightclub

Imagine a low rectangular building made entirely of M.D.C. concrete whose only windows are narrow slits and whose only entrance and exit are two massive blast doors (800 M.D.C. each), and you have the nightclub known as the Bunker. It is a popular dance club that has become a chain that can be found in various 'Burbs, usually near the border of an Old Town and New Town or a busy intersection. It is a place where a wide range of people can meet, mingle, dance and unwind. The Bunker Nightclubs strike such a nice balance and have enough class and atmosphere that young Old Towners and New Towners, humans and D-Bees, young people and older clientele (30s and 40s, though usually criminals) find it equally appealing. The fact that D-Bees are allowed and known criminals and street gangs frequent these establishments gives them an edge and sense of excitement that few other clubs out in the open can claim. Like some of the elite, posh clubs of the pre-Rifts era, customers stand in a line that can wrap around the building. The nightclub manager or his "spotters" go out to eyeball the crowd, picking out the beautiful and interesting people for admittance as they go along. Those not chosen get to advance in the line and wait for untold hours until they are either selected in one of the later reviews or the club thins out enough to let in the less desirable clubbers. The music at each is live and may include local acts and/or traveling entertainers. The pay for performers is very good, attracting the better groups.

One of the unique and fun aspects of the Bunker is that its patrons dress up in outrageous, sexy and provocative costumes, which include take-offs on garments worn by practitioners of magic or costumes that make the wearer resemble a D-Bee, demon or other inhuman creature. The CS authorities are not thrilled with this idea but tolerate it. This dress code helps the real McCoys to blend into the crowd and offers a comfort zone most illegal facilities don't provide. Additionally, the thick, bunker-like M.D.C. construction keeps the sights and sounds of the party inside off the streets, and the happenings locked inside, a feature that the people inside love ("Wow, nobody knows what's going on in here.") and the residents and businesses welcome ("God, I don't want to know what's going on in there."). Likewise, the dense M.D.C. walls prevent gunfire and magic that may erupt from a brawl that has gotten way out of hand from spilling into the street and causing injury or property damage.

The idea of the Bunker Nightclub chain originated with the son of a recently deceased crime lord, *Rex Baxter*, otherwise known as "Frag" because of his love for explosives and incendiary devices, and the two M.D.C. fragmentation grenades he always carries. Frag had a vision. A vision to provide booze and drugs to the masses and get them so hooked that they would come pounding on his door begging for more. His goal that was realized with the creation of the Bunker Nightclub chain, the brainchild of his well-dressed partner, Roger "the Razor" Carmichael, a retired member of the Coalition's Special Warfare Division.

The two have managed to get this idea past the Coalition authorities by selling them on the concept that if the people stay drunk, drugged up and partying the night away from midnight till sunrise, and sleep half the day away, they are less likely to become involved in subversive activities or be attracted to the wrong kind of people, like Rogue Scholars. Both could care less about the effects drugs and alcohol have on their patrons or how it impacts their families and the community, nor do they really care about stopping subversives and civil unrest for the sake of the CS – they're in it for the fame and money. As impossible as it may sound, they sold the CS on it with the proviso that they report any dissident factions to the I.S.S. and allow undercover agents to operate unimpeded in the clubs. Since the CS is looking for dissidents and not criminals, drug operations or even D-Bees, the relationship has been a booming success that has lasted five years now and going strong. To Frag and Razor, most of these people are little more than vermin to them anyway, while they see themselves as some kind of entrepreneurial geniuses. The people, of course, know nothing about any of this and just see Frag and Razor as fellow party animals and the leaders in cutting edge entertainment. Both are flashy dresser, ladies' men and enjoy hobnobbing with up and coming crime lords, though Razor tends to eschew the limelight, appearing only from to time at the most avant-garde and prestigious events.

The Bunker, itself, also has a double life and is much more than it seems. There are three levels under the dance floor, accessible only from an entrance shaft covered by a multi-ton M.D.C. slab which is hidden among some bushes right next to the club. An elevator platform rises to the surface to carry supplies and troops to the appropriate level. You see, the Bunker

Nightclub chain (there are currently nine) serve as a series of super-secret, secure Coalition munitions warehouses designed by CS Army engineers to survive a full-scale, military style attack. If martial law is declared or if the fortress city fell to an enemy force, Coalition troops could move in and have a secure, easily defensible command post in the 'Burbs. Each "nightclub" contains enough weapons, ammo and gear to equip an entire military battalion, complete with communications center, sick bay, water purification, independent energy system and a platoon of SAMAS power armor. The CS builds these bunkers under a false company known as *Concrete Entertainment*, presumably part of the Bunker Nightclub empire based in the Old Town of Josephton. Frag and Razor have no idea that their Bunker Nightclubs are, well, military bunkers part of a CS failsafe strategy – nobody does. They foolishly believe the CS is so absolutely sold on their stupid nightclub idea that the government is secretly willing to build their clubs for them at no cost. How could they pass up a deal like that?

Adventure Hooks: Frag and Razor, particularly Frag, are into all kinds of illegal and underworld stuff, mostly through association with others. They can get away with it because the CS looks the other way to just about anything they do. As long as the two do not engage in or support any subversive activities, they can, literally, get away with murder. This gives these two a tremendous amount of freedom and power, though neither one realizes it, nor exploits more than a small fraction of that power. Why? Because they are much too caught up in being cult figure celebrities, socializing, getting drunk, being important and making money; which is why the CS agreed to this venture in the first place. To the CS, Frag and Razor are the perfect, highly paid, public stooges and front-men for an operation they know nothing about. Consequently, all kinds of violence, drug use, drug deals, fights, duels, murders, crimes and decadence take place inside the clubs (and never suspecting for a second that it is happening above a secret Coalition Army depot). The CS doesn't care because they are glad to see D-Bees, free thinkers, rogues and troublemakers destroy themselves, and because it is the absolutely perfect cover for them, and they are right. **Note:** While all kinds of trouble, crime and adventure may take place inside the Bunker Nightclubs, the one scenario that will *not* happen is the CS underground bunker and weapons being discovered. (And if it was, 30 Skelebots instantly come to life to hold the depot, a silent alarm alerts the Army at Chi-Town and a platoon or a company of CS armored troops arrive to keep the bunker under their control. This happens in 2D4 minutes with a wing of SAMAS arriving in under two minutes. In the case of such an unfortunate event, *all* patrons inside the club are prevented from leaving and are summarily executed so the secret of the military bunkers is preserved. Nobody on the street can see or hear what is happening inside, so the CS can pin the entire event on a Tolkeen or Federation of Magic terrorist attack with an alarming number of casualties, "who shall be avenged!" The only exception to the "kill everyone" contingency are Frag and Razor who will be Mind Wiped by a CS Mind Melter and the appropriate memories of a terrorist attack implanted.

15. Michael's School of Self-Defense

Various forms of unarmed combat are taught at this school, including all of the following: Boxing, Wrestling, Gymnastics,

Body Building, W.P. Staff, W.P. Blunt, W.P. Chain, Basic Hand to Hand, Expert Hand to Hand and Martial Arts Hand to Hand Combat skills. The school is run by *Michael Liu* and his three sons and three daughters. If a student shows a particular aptitude and strong leadership abilities, he may be invited to meet Master Liu personally. Then, if Master Liu is impressed, the student may be offered entrance into the Special Training School, either to develop him into an instructor or to teach him armed forms of combat, including the sword and/or bow. The building is a reasonable size with a gymnastics wing and regular, full-sized gymnasium. Students range from ages 6-66, with the majority being 14-30; *humans only*.

Adventure Hooks: Any of the following could be true, or not.

1. The Coalition authorities have been suspicious about the school for years and frequently drop in without warning to watch the workouts for a while or to inspect the facility and question some of the students, parents and instructors. So far, the school has checked out as clean as a whistle every time, and there have easily been a hundred surprise visits over the last two years alone.

2. A persistent rumor is that Michael Liu was once a master instructor for the Cyber-Knights and is a good friend of Lord Coake and a number of other famous Knights. Another is that Liu is, himself, a retired or disillusioned Cyber-Knight. If true, it had to be years ago, because Michael Liu has lived in the Chi-Town 'Burbs for more than 25 years, and in Firetown for the last 15. The CS has tried to follow up this story but can find no information on anyone named Michael Liu, or fitting his description, ever having been involved with the Cyber-Knights.

3. Rumor: The Liu family has a secret sanctuary where they hide and protect visiting Cyber-Knights and other heroes.

4. Michael Liu has three other children, two boys and a girl who are Cyber-Knights.

5. Michael, two of his children and a couple of other instructors secretly instruct D-Bees in the martial arts. However, there is no official building for these instructions. Classes are moved from place to place every couple of weeks, or whenever they feel necessary. One time classes are held in an abandoned warehouse, next time in building owned by a trusted friend, the next, in a local gymnasium after hours, or in a secluded area of a park, or a parking structure late at night, and so on. An oath of secrecy is required of each student.

16. Calmoth and the Big-C Wilderness Shop

This is a small shop that sells stuffed wild animals, and animal antlers, horns, teeth, claws, skulls, and skins, as well as a good selection of animal traps, snares, fishing and hunting gear, and wilderness supplies (rope, canteens, sleeping bags, tents, etc.). In a lot of ways, the Big-C Wilderness Shop is like an army surplus store, only for hunters and trappers. The prices are reasonable, the quality good, and it attracts a fair number of adventurers, woodsmen and Psi-Stalkers to keep the canine's head above water.

Calmoth is a canine from another world (a Palladium Wolfen) passing himself off as a large Dog Boy, retired from active service. He is on the run, hiding from his older brother Calbuck (a Cyber-Knight), and came to the 'Burbs figuring that his brother would not follow him here. Calmoth is a third-generation Rifts-Earth Wolfen. His grandparents were part of a pack from the Palladium World that arrived through a Rift and settled in the North American southwest. When Calmoth was just a cub, his idol, protector, and role model was his oldest brother, Calbuck.

The pack's finest athlete, hunter, tracker, and warrior, Calbuck was the fair-furred boy. It came as a surprise to no member of the clan that Calbuck would eventually succeed in attaining the status of a Cyber-Knight. It was after Calbuck became a Cyber-Knight and returned to his pack for a visit that things went terribly wrong for Calmoth.

Although on the smallish side for his people, Calmoth was a valued member of the pack, whose Major psychic abilities of a Psi-Sensitive were often of great value. Unfortunately, these talents made him too vulnerable to the effects of *Psi-Cola* and ultimately led him into addiction.

Nevertheless, Calmoth was able to hide his addiction from family and friends for a long time, until he followed his brother on a mission to pursue some brigands. Calbuck took some of his men and set off as a scouting party, leaving Calmoth behind with the rest of the group. The Cyber-Knight figured that Calmoth's psychic talents would make him the perfect sentry.

Unfortunately, after downing a couple jugs of Psi-Cola he had smuggled in, Calmoth passed out and his comrades were attacked by a band of brigands. Unconscious, Calmoth was ignored by the invaders, but many others were killed. Unfortunately for Calmoth, a few of his other comrades survived to tell the returning Calbuck about his brother's deadly sloth and folly.

When Calmoth heard that Calbuck was enraged enough to kill him, rather than fight the brother he had always loved and respected, he fled. Eventually, Calmoth ended up in the Chi-Town 'Burbs and has remained ever since, eking out a living and hoping that he is never forced to face the brother he feels he betrayed. Further complicating matters is that Calmoth is still a Psi-Cola junkie.

G.M.'s Notes: Unknown to Calmoth, Calbuck no longer wants to kill him. The Cyber-Knight was enraged when he first found out about his brother's addiction and the death of some of his friends due to it. If he had found Calmoth a year or two ago, the two brothers would have enacted a rendition of Cain and Abel. Since then, Calbuck has spent time at Tolkeen helping out with rescue efforts and has seen enough mortal weakness, death and families torn apart forever. It has softened his heart and he wishes to forgive his brother. Calbuck plans on thrashing Calmoth to within an inch of his life for getting addicted to Psi-Cola and do whatever it takes to help his brother beat the addiction. Ultimately, Calbuck wants a brother who is clean and sober, not a corpse and some unpleasant memories. Right now he has other pressing matters, but someday he will make things right.

Adventure Hooks: 1. Calmoth is as addicted to Psi-Cola as ever. If not, his business would be thriving, but he spends a full third of his income on the stuff and half his time in a stupor. If the Cyber-Knight brother learns of this, he may hire a group of adventurers to get Calmoth "clean." This could be an adventure

in and of itself (played for laughs or deadly serious), and probably best accomplished by making Calmoth a (NPC) part of the team.

2. The player characters, probably in the wilderness, away from the 'Burbs, encounter a half crazed Calmoth who begs them to take him back to Firetown, please! He promises to pay them (with money he doesn't have) and tells them how he was abducted by madmen and needs to home and get fix. In truth, it was scenario #1 above, but he leaves out the parts about his addiction and his brother hiring folks to help him. Calmoth will be both a help and a hindrance during any adventures he may accompany the group on during the trip home, and if it takes long enough, he might actually go through sufficient detox to break the hold of the Psi-Cola addiction – unless he gets his hands on some sooner, and he'll steal to get it, possibly getting the group into trouble. Additionally, the first group hired by his brother is looking for him and Calmoth's lies may lead to the player group and these other adventurers getting into a skirmish.

3. Calmoth gets a loose tongue after drinking enough Psi-Cola and will tell a drinking buddy (the buddy can drink something other than Psi-Cola, though the canine can't understand why) rumors and things that he knows about. These could be leads for adventure. Likewise, Calmoth may lead them into trouble when out of his head.

4. May get into adventures and trouble doing favors for Psi-Cola dealers in order to get paid in the stuff.

Calmoth Quick Stats

Alignment: Was scrupulous, but his addiction has turned him into Anarchist.

Attributes: I.Q. 12, M.A. 9, M.E. 7, P.S. 23, P.P. 14, P.E. 15, P.B. 10, Spd. 20 (was 31, but his weight and laziness has brought it down; will return if he can kick Psi-Cola and lose 200 lbs/90 kg).

Height: 7 feet, 3 inches (2.21 m) (smallish for a Wolfen but towers over most Dog Boys).

Weight: 530 pounds (238.5); guzzling Psi-Cola by the barrel gives one a gut.

P.P.E.: 11. **I.S.P.:** 67.

Disposition: A lazy, slow moving (reduce speed and P.P. by half) mellow space cadet when high, a hyper whiner when in need of a fix, and a pretty good guy inbetween.

Experience Level: 5th level Wilderness Scout.

Skills of Note: All the typical O.C.C. skills plus Basic Math, W.P. Pole Arm, W.P. Energy Rifle and Hand to Hand: Expert.

Magic Knowledge: None.

Psionic Powers: Intuitive Combat (10), Mind Block (4), See Aura (6), See the Invisible (4), Sense Evil (2), Sense Magic (3), Sense Time (2) and Sixth Sense.

Money: Rarely more than 3D6x10, everything goes to buying Psi-Cola and running the business, in that order.

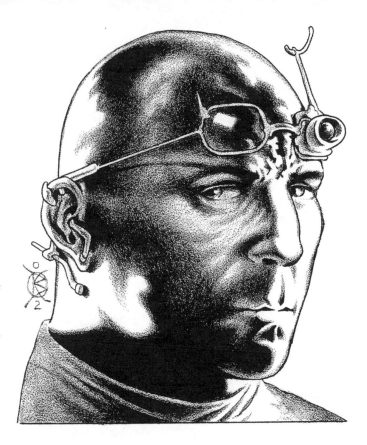

17. The Meat Market (Body-Chop-Shop)

The Meat Market is ostensibly a butcher shop with a large selection of meats, including beef, pork, lamb, lunch meats (pressed and smoked), and sausages, along with some breads and drinks. Price are low to average with a special deal on ground "Mystery Meat" believed to be part beef, pork and chicken (some say horse, others rat, and others human!). Although Dr. Panach and his fellow "butchers" adamantly refuse to divulge the ingredients of this meat (claiming it's a trade secret), their prices are so good that they regularly manage to sell nearly their entire stocks and have developed a loyal following.

However, the Meat Market is actually a front for the *Pan-Man Body-Chop-Shop*. Dr. Virgil Panach, a Cyber-Doc, acts the part of the owner and head butcher, and took the time and effort to study the meat cutting and packing business, so he pulls off the role quite convincingly. Cybernetic and bionic enhancement is where the really big money is, however, and is Doctor Panach's true love. Dr. Panach considers Cyber-Medicine to be his calling, but he also enjoys his masquerade as a butcher and sees to it that his customers receive good quality meats and service.

Adventure Hooks:

1. Connections to the Black Market provide Doctor Panach with a full range of bionic services. Anyone up for a full bionic conversion? Partial reconstruction? Implants maybe? He's having a sale on cosmetic cybernetics – 25% off list price.

2. Rumor: The Mystery Meat to augment the Meat Market's stock and is a means of getting rid of incriminating evidence (i.e. is the ground up body parts taken from patients getting bionic replacement limbs). Gross. Does anyone really want to learn if this is true?

3. Meetings and clashes with Cyber-Snatchers, Headhunters, Cyborgs and City Rats can start here. The good doctor regularly buys "used" bionics and implants.

4. Rumor: Doctor Panach may be responsible for disappearances and kidnapings when the victim had bionics or several cybernetic systems. Word on the street is that the Doc regularly hires Cyber-Snatchers and evil D-Bees to "acquire" used equipment for him.

5. Rumor: Doctor Panach is really a UTI alien that survived the Juicer Uprising. If true, what else is he up to and are there others of his kind in Firetown?

6. Rumor: The Doctor will install bionics for free if one is willing to let him experiment and do as he pleases.

Doctor Panach Quick Stats

Real Name: Dr. Virgil Panach.

Alignment: Aberrant evil.

Attributes: I.Q. 13, M.E. 15, M.A. 11, P.S. 9, P.P. 14, P.E. 15, P.B. 12, Spd. 7

Hit Points: 45. **S.D.C.:** 7.

Weight: 215 pounds (96.7 kg). **Height:** 5 feet, 9 inches (1.75 m). **Age:** 48. **P.P.E.:** 7.

Disposition: Dr. Panach considers himself to be a rebel against an oppressive system, using his medical skills and knowledge to aid a downtrodden populace. Dr. Panach sincerely feels that his actions are benefitting both his patients and society in general. He sees nothing wrong with anything he's done. The doctor is genial and friendly to his meat market customers but projects an air of competence and confidence to his cybernetic patients.

Experience Level: 8th level Cyber-Doc.

Magic Knowledge: None. **Psionic Powers:** None.

Combat Skills: Hand to Hand: Basic.

Attacks per Melee: Five.

Bonuses: +1 to strike, +2 to parry, +2 to dodge, +2 to damage, +2 to roll with impact/to pull punch, critical strike on a 19-20, kick attack, and judo-style body throw/flip.

Weapon Proficiencies: W.P. Auto. Pistol, W.P. Energy Pistol, and W.P. Knife, all at 8th level proficiency.

Skills of Note: Literacy in American 95%, Speaks Latin 98%, Medical Doctor 95/85%, M.D. in Cybernetics 95/98%, Pathology 85%, Biology 85%, Chemistry 75%, Computer Operation 80%, Mathematics: Advanced 90%, Read and Use Sensory Equipment 80%, and Pilot Automobile 80%.

Weapons & Armor: Dr. Panach is a healer and avoids combat if at all possible. However, he does keep a Vibro-Knife and some pistols (both automatic and energy) nearby for protection of himself and his patients if the need arises. Dr. Panach has a suit of Plastic-Man armor stowed away in case he makes a house call in a particularly dangerous area. He is also protected by an insane Headhunter named Butch, turned nurse (7th level, Diabolic), and a light, full conversion cyborg who looks completely human, named Cleo (5th level 'Borg, Anarchist). Both are loyal to the Doctor and Cleo and the Doc are becoming more than friends.

Cybernetics: The right arm is bionic with several bionic features, including a scalpel finger, laser finger, camera finger, retractable utility arms, and a wrist hypodermic needle system. Implants include a headjack, enhanced hearing, gyro-compass, clock calendar and a Type AA-1 with an ASH supplemental cyber-disguise.

Money: Has 36.7 million credits stashed away and his meat business pulls in an easy 1.3 million credits a year. He also has an expensive home in Prosekville, a sport car, hovercycle and motor boat. He is a frequent patron of the Park Gentlemen's Club.

Description: A portly middle-aged man with a shaved head. He will almost always be wearing something in white (whether it is a surgical gown or a butcher's apron), and often a multi-optics system.

18. The Psi-Cola Man

"What, you're a psychic who'd like to score some good Psi-Cola? Well, my man, you came to the right place! Billy Bosco's the name and Psi-Cola's my game! I've got the sweetest batch of Psi-Cola you've ever tasted and, for the right price, I can supply you with as much Psi-Cola as you'll ever need for as long as you need it. Remember the name, Billy Bosco, the Psi-Cola Man!"

That upbeat sales pitch belongs to Billy Bosco, the self-proclaimed "king" of the Psi-Cola sellers. Billy's got cases of the stuff and is willing to sell it off at bargain prices. Billy is new to the Chi-Town 'Burbs and works out of his new apartment (wherever he is staying at for the moment), a local café or restaurant, right out on the street, out of the back of his van, or anywhere that is convenient for the customer. The word on the street is out, "If you need Psi-Cola, go see Billy Bosco!"

Unfortunately, the snappy sales pitch is a pack of lies (just like everything else about Billy Bosco). The truth of the matter is that, no matter how much Billy implies (or claims outright) to be the new Psi-Cola representative for the Chi-Town area, Billy is a small-time hustler who has no connection with the real producers and distributors of Psi-Cola.

Billy Reinhardt was eking out a living as a smuggler. Although the job kept him clothed and fed, it also kept him from reaching his true potential (so he thought). Billy always worked as an underling and felt that he was capable of so much more if he could only get the chance to prove himself. He figured his talent for seeing the "big picture" should qualify him for a leadership position. His superiors, however, saw things differently, and felt Billy's penchant for grandiose schemes and reluctance to deal with minor details made him a recipe for disaster.

Recently, Billy was part of a crew that had smuggled a big shipment of Psi-Cola into the Chi-Town 'Burbs. As low man in the group, Billy was assigned to stay with the truck while his co-workers went to meet with their buyers and set up the final exchange. This was a lucky break for Billy because the I.S.S. were waiting for the drug traffickers. There was a brief shoot-out and, within a matter of minutes, Billy Reinhardt's colleagues were dead.

Sitting by himself at a bar and staring at one of the Cola bottles, Billy pondered what to do next when a gruff voice hailed him. It turned out to be a Dog Boy whose keen sense of smell detected the scent of Psi-Cola. After a little bit of dickering, Billy made his first sale and decided that this was his golden opportunity – he would sell the Psi-Cola shipment himself and reap all of the profits. Since then, Billy has taken on the street handle of "Bosco" (he got this from a broken sign that he passed. The sign originally said "Talibos Company," not that this means anything to Billy, it just sounded good to him) and has been trying to pass himself off as the new area distributor of Psi-Cola.

Billy is out to make a quick score and then get out of town. Although his supply of Psi-Cola is limited to what was in the truck and he has no way of getting any more, Billy has been readily promising his customers that he can obtain all they need with no problem. He intends to be long gone when the junkies realize that their source has dried up. Billy has been very aggressive in hawking his wares but, because of his typical lack of attention to details, he has no idea of how much in over his head he really is. Although Billy knows about avoiding the I.S.S., he has not considered problems from other areas, such as:

1. His customers are addicts, not morons. If any of them see past his lines of bull, they may decide to eliminate this pain in the butt and take all the Psi-Cola for themselves. Even the ones who are convinced that Billy Bosco is the real thing are desperate. So far, no one has been desperate enough to try to rip off Billy but that could change.

2. If Billy's former employers (the people who sent the Psi-Cola shipment to Chi-Town in the first place) ever find out that one of their smugglers survived, with the merchandise no less, while all the others were killed in a Coalition ambush, they may assume that as the sole survivor, he set up the rest of the crew to steal the shipment and sell it himself. Although this is not true and Billy had nothing to do with the I.S.S. being there, they will come gunning for him.

3. Any of the actual Psi-Cola pushers who normally service the area may figure out this new guy is a fake and come after him. He's stomping all over their turf and they don't like it. Junkies, like Calmoth (and those trying to help him, like the player characters) and innocent people, could get caught in the crossfire.

Billy Bosco Quick Stats

If Billy Bosco lived some 500 years earlier, he would have sold snake oil. A con artist with a glib line, Billy is always on the lookout for the best deal he can get. Other people are simply there to be used for his advantage.

Real Name: William "Billy" Reinhardt.

Alignment: Miscreant evil.

Attributes: I.Q. 10, M.E. 14, M.A. 13, P.S. 11, P.P. 9, P.E. 12, P.B. 12, Spd. 13

Hit Points: 34. **S.D.C.:** 17.

Weight: 175 pounds (79 kg). **Height:** 6 feet (1.8 m). **Age:** 24. **P.P.E.:** 9.

Disposition: Billy is a schemer who likes to take chances. He is overconfident of his ability to talk his way out of almost any situation and is not the big picture guy he thinks he is. Still, he talks a good game and thinks quick on his feet. If he wasn't always looking for his big break he might rise through the ranks to a mid-level position, but he's too impatient and cocky for that.

Experience Level: 6th level Smuggler.

Magic Knowledge: None. **Psionic Powers:** None.

Combat Skills: Hand to Hand: Basic.

Attacks per Melee: Five.

Bonuses: +1 to strike, +2 to parry, +2 to dodge, +2 to roll with impact/to pull punch, critical strike on a 19-20, kick attack, +1 on initiative when palming or involving streetwise or concealment.

Weapon Proficiencies: W.P. Energy Pistol and W.P. Knife, both at 6th level proficiency.

Skills of Note: Literacy in American 75%, Speaks Euro, Gobblely, Spanish, and Techno-Can, all at 95%, Mathematics: Basic 98%, Concealment 50%, Detect Ambush 70%, Detect Concealment 60%, Disguise 60%, Escape Artist 60%, Palming 55%, Streetwise 56%, Streetwise: Drugs 50%, Radio: Basic 85%, Radio: Scramblers 70%, Cryptography 60%, Computer Operation 80%, Pilot Truck 65%, Prowl 50%, and Running, Automotive Mechanics 50%.

Weapons & Armor: Billy prefers to talk his way out of tense situations rather than fighting. However, he will carry some type of energy pistol and a Vibro-Knife for protection. Billy has never worn armor nor does he intend to.

Money: Right now he's making money hand over fist. He has 290,000 in credits, 80,000 in trade goods (mostly electronics), lives in a large, furnished, rented home (as indicated on the map), and has bought himself an impressive wardrobe, entertainment system and hover-van totaling around 250 grand all by itself.

Description: An average-looking man with long, dark hair tied back in a ponytail. In the past, Billy was perennially dressed informally (i.e. in leathers and such). Since "hitting the big time" (as he feels it), Billy now dresses "fashionably," like he's a real player.

19. Banner Orphanage

Also known as the "Big House"

A four story facility that is the largest orphanage in town with 1700-1800 children at any time and room for as many as 2200. It is a highly disciplined, extremely well organized and apparently well financed operation. Like *Camp Fireplace*, it has a certain faction of troublemakers, thieves and City Rats operating out of the place, but they are generally less precocious or experienced than the kids at the Camp, and less well informed (only tapped into 1D6x10% of the current rumor mill at any given time and only really know the northern part of town near the orphanage). The highly skilled rogues of Camp Fireplace are constantly competing with and showing up the City Rats at Banner, and think of "the Big House" as a place for *sissies* and *crybabies.*

The reason the rogue faction at Banner is less experienced is because the folks who run the orphanage are much better staffed and more strict. They give the children uniforms, all the basics and plenty of love and discipline, but they also keep them in check as much as possible. This is done both for the welfare of the kids and to keep their secret operations from being discovered. You see, Banner is also an underground school and a haven for D-Bee orphans funded, in part, by sympathizers from the city of Lazlo. In this particular instance, the school and

D-Bee orphanages are literally underground, located in a secret subterranean complex built by Earth Warlocks and friends from Lazlo. The two level underground facility is located 60 feet (18.3 m) beneath the basement of the orphanage and is accessible via magic or four concealed shafts and one, long diagonal tunnel. It has a cafeteria-style kitchen and dining area, large supply storage room, large playroom, meeting hall, gymnasium with a stage for performance, nine classrooms, a library (yes, of books), offices, an infirmary and an indoor garden with grass, flowering plants, bushes and a few trees. It is kept alive with magically installed sunlight that follows the pattern of the sun. In fact, half the underground complex uses a Techno-Wizard sunlight system of lighting as well as a TW quiet, solar powered generator and air filtration system.

Chosen children (those who are intelligent or gifted and can keep a secret; roughly 10-15%) in the surface orphanage are secretly taught how to read and write in special classes, but not in the underground. The underground orphanage is used to house 180-240 D-Bee children, half of whom are taught to read and write. The rest of the "students" in the underground school are adults, humans and D-Bees, cultivated from trusted friends and acquaintances who wish to become literate. There is a library with books for teaching how to read and write as well as over 300 books on various other subjects, including the complete works of Erin Tarn, volumes on Earth's real history, and a number of highly collectable pre-Rifts books, plus an additional 700 books on computer disk. Adult classes are kept small to avoid attention and are snuck in, in groups of 20-40 at a time. A course in reading is usually 12 weeks, three days a week, 3-4 hours per session. After the fundamentals are taught, the students are sent off to pursue furthering their reading skills on their own. Only helpers at the school and orphanage, and special cases are allowed to continue their studies in the secret facility.

Adventure Hooks: 1. Coalition Authorities in the ISS are suspicious of the orphanage's funding and try to keep an eye on the place to see if they can notice anything unusual from a distance. A few ISS undercover officers have gone so far as to pose as prospective adopting parents to snoop around inside the orphanage, but have failed to uncover anything untoward. Neither have a few surprise raids. Still they watch and wonder. If an ISS officer should learn something damaging, he would need to be silenced before he could spread the word. That doesn't necessarily mean killed. He could be psionically Mind Wiped, Hypnotized, etc., to forget what he learned (or paid off, threatened to stay silent or, if necessary, terminated).

2. Since Banner is heavily financed by friends in Lazlo, the place is also used as a safe house for visiting practitioners of magic and adventurers on assignment from Lazlo. They are usually kept in the underground levels or pose as a visiting friend, temporary worker, or prospective adopting parent. Likewise, practitioners of magic from or with ties to Lazlo may turn to Banner for medical assistance or a place to hide out in case of emergencies. Of course, such activities place the orphanage and the kids in jeopardy whenever they happen. The folks who run the operation are incredibly discreet and well organized but someday something will go wrong and when it does . . .

3. If the Coalition authorities ever find out about the secret D-Bee orphanage, the literacy school or the orphanage's connection with the magic kingdom of Lazlo, there will be Hell to pay.